Rebuilt Green

THE NATURAL CAPITAL CENTER AND THE TRANSFORMATIVE POWER OF BUILDING

JEAN VOLLUM NATURAL CAPITAL CENTER

RebuiltGreen

THE NATURAL CAPITAL CENTER AND THE TRANSFORMATIVE POWER OF BUILDING

CONTRIBUTORS

Spencer B. Beebe
Rob Bennett
Stuart Cowan
Ralph DiNola
Eugénie Frerichs
Erin Kellogg
Bob Naito
Michael O'Brien
Bettina von Hagen

EDITORS

Bettina von Hagen, Erin Kellogg, and Eugénie Frerichs

DESIGNER

Melissa Tatge

A PUBLICATION OF

PORTLAND, OREGON

Building Salmon Nation

JEAN VOLLUM NATURAL CAPITAL CENTER
721 NW NINTH AVENUE, SUITE 200
PORTLAND, OR 97209

TEL 503.227.6225 | FAX 503.222.1517
INFO@ECOTRUST.ORG | WWW.ECOTRUST.ORG

Founded in 1991 and based in Portland, Oregon, Ecotrust is a non-profit organization working with individuals, organizations, businesses, agencies, and tribes along the Pacific Coast of North America to build Salmon Nation, a place where people and wild salmon thrive.

First Edition
Printed in Portland, Oregon, United States of America

Library of Congress Card Number: 2003108722
ISBN 0-9676364-2-6

The text of this book is set in Century Gothic.

NEW LEAF PAPER

ENVIRONMENTAL BENEFITS STATEMENT

This book is printed on New Leaf Reincarnation Matte, made with 100% recycled fiber, 50% post-consumer waste, processed chlorine free. By using this environmentally friendly paper, Ecotrust saved the following resources:

trees	water	energy	solid waste	greenhouse gases
21 fully grown	4,668 gallons	14 million BTUs	1,022 pounds	1,581 pounds

Calculated based on research done by Environmental Defense and other members of the Paper Task Force.

© New Leaf Paper Visit us in cyberspace at www.newleafpaper.com or call 1-888-989-5323

CREDITS

Cover and book design: Melissa Tatge

Sketches and architectural renderings: Jonathan Meendering

Printer: Paramount Graphics, Portland, OR

Photos and diagrams:

Samuel Beebe: Pages 16, 23, 27, 33 (curb), 51, 58, 59, 64, 67, 71, 94, 95, 103, 104, 108, 109, 111, 113

Melissa Tatge: Cover; pages 17, 25, 28, 33 (bikes and HVAC), 35, 37, 48, 57, 73, 74, 78, 81 (ecoroof #4), 87, 101

Dan Tyrpak: Pages 8, 13, 14, 15, 34, 40, 45, 46, 50, 88, 89, 102

p. 7 Courtesy of Spencer B. Beebe; p. 9 Howard Silverman; p. 11 © Michael Wilhelm; p. 12 Spencer B. Beebe; p. 19 Courtesy of Venerable Properties, © Michael Gonzalez; p. 20 Courtesy of Environmental Building Supply; p. 21 Courtesy of The ReBuilding Center of Our United Villages; p. 22 Prairie Holdings Corporation (Prairie Crossing), Innovative Design Inc. (Selma Middle School); Local Government Commission (Village Homes); Herman Miller (Herman Miller Greenhouse); University of British Columbia (C.K. Choi); Daniel Lipow (Audubon House); p. 24 Courtesy of ShoreBank Enterprise Pacific; p. 26 Courtesy of the City of Seattle; p. 30 Green Building Services; p. 36 City of Portland G/Rated; p. 38 Oregon Historical Society; p. 41 Oregon Historical Society; p. 43 Oregon Historical Society; p. 55 Courtesy of Holst Architecture (floor plans); p. 65 Jonathan Meendering; p. 77 City of Portland G/Rated; p. 80 Jonathan Meendering; p. 82 City of Portland G/Rated; p. 83 Stormwater Management, Inc.; p. 84 Courtesy of Atelier Dreiseitl; p. 85 Patrick Condon, University of British Columbia; p.86 Lowell Downey; p.90 Iisaak Forest Resouurces; p. 99 Spencer B. Beebe; p. 107 Howard Silverman; p. 117 Sophia von Hagen

Contents

PREFACE

by Spencer B. Beebe

In a meeting at her Toronto home this spring, author and former Ecotrust board member Jane Jacobs and I searched for reasons to be optimistic about the way the world was going. Perhaps we need a revolution to turn things around, I mused. But Jane countered with more sober words.

"Good things come from evolution, not revolution; from building up new things, not tearing old things down," Jane said. She reminded me that civilizations need farms, forests, and rivers to support dense populations in the cities, and that cities repay the favor by getting lots of heads together to innovate and invent. Whether one's concern is natural ecosystems or economic systems, density propels evolution.

As an environmentalist, I found it challenging to embrace Jane Jacob's ideas when we first met almost a decade ago. I had created Ecotrust to protect large pristine watersheds in the coastal temperate rain forests of North America, not to practice urban renewal. But my colleagues and I recognized from the outset that our success would require the support of local people who saw conservation in their own self-interest. When Jane joined our board, she helped us understand that this rural constituency would be strengthened by purposeful connections to markets, technology, and capital in the cities.

As a Portland resident who has spent a lifetime leaving town in search of the solitude of wilderness, I've been forced to admit that the city has become more humane and interesting over time. As Portland grew in size, diversity, and sophistication, Ecotrust began to question its relationship to its home city and neighborhood. What could we do, right here, to create a marketplace for the ideas, goods, and services of the conservation economy?

In the end, Ecotrust's own self-interest was behind this question. We wanted a home. We wanted to own, not rent. We dreamed of a capital base of our own, and a resource strategy that would yield confidence, continuity, and new opportunities to learn and earn. Status and recognition? That might be nice, too. We wanted to be part of the community and the restoration process underway in our neighborhood. If we could make a good case for the merits of green building, shouldn't we do it ourselves?

Early in 1997, I took these half-formed ambitions to another Ecotrust board member and philanthropist in the west hills of Portland. Jean Vollum knew a far-fetched idea when she saw it, but perhaps she saw some new sparkle in my eyes that day as well. Jean made an unprecedented gift to Ecotrust that allowed us to purchase the century-old McCraken Warehouse in the heart of the rapidly redeveloping River District of Northwest Portland.

Several board members, a significant number of the staff, and pretty much all our donors thought we were nuts. One board member suggested we were betting the organization on unreinforced masonry on a well-documented seismic fault. The next three years were hard ones. Several times, I thought we had finally bitten off more than we could chew. But our board and staff stayed with us. Our development team led by Bettina von Hagen, Bob Naito, and Bob Walsh proved more than equal to the challenge. Ecotrust council member Stewart Brand, author of *How Buildings Learn*, guided our first design charette and encouraged us forward. Our friends and supporters stood by us, the City of Portland found ways to encourage us, and our new neighbors put up with us. Our tenants cast the final, crucial votes of confidence as, one by one, they signed leases and joined our vision.

We broke ground in February 2000, and soon discovered the tangible and immediate satisfactions of removing lead-based paint, re-pointing old brick, and building new doors and windows out of recycled old growth Douglas-fir. On a propitious day eighteen months later, the Jean Vollum Natural Capital Center opened for business.

At the grand opening, our anchor tenant, Patagonia's owner and founder Yvon Chouinard, startled the assembled audience of friends, dignitaries, and curious passers-by when he said "the most responsible way to buy clothes is to shop at Goodwill. And the most responsible way to build is to recycle an old building."

Maybe we had done the right thing after all. Like a healthy ecosystem, the Jean Vollum Natural Capital Center combines density, diversity, and connectedness to make something greater than the sum of its parts. It's the kind of place we can gather good heads to think up new ideas, to rebuild, and perhaps even to evolve, just a little, towards a better future. It's the kind of place that gives Jane Jacobs, and me, hope.

Spencer B. Beebe
Portland, Oregon
June 2003

Spencer Beebe and Jane Jacobs, Middle Fork, Salmon River, Summer 1997.

ECOTRUST
JEAN VOLLUM
NATURAL CAPITAL
CENTER

INTRODUCTION

by Bettina von Hagen, Erin Kellogg and Eugénie Frerichs

This is a book about a building: the Jean Vollum Natural Capital Center — one building among many in a rapidly changing neighborhood in northwest Portland, Oregon. This building's story began over a century ago as an important river, rail, and then trucking distribution center. This was followed by a period of decline and virtual abandon, and then, in recent times, renewal. As the latest owners of the building, we at Ecotrust chose to redevelop this nineteenth century warehouse in a way that would respect the earliest chapters of its history, but would also embrace, and indeed push the bounds of twenty-first century technology and ideas. With an ambitious vision, we have added a few chapters to the building's story. Today it stands as a building of light, air, and water; a building that is highly adapted to its purpose and its place.

Ecotrust was created in 1991 to help focus attention and resources on the ecologically significant and highly threatened coastal temperate rain forest of North America's Pacific coast. We worked initially in rural, coastal communities from Prince William Sound in Alaska to San Francisco, helping individuals, businesses, and organizations begin to build a **conservation economy**. Our activities ranged from financing sustainably-managed forests to cleaning up and redeveloping toxic brownfield sites to restoring watersheds. Almost all of our projects led us back to the region's cities in search of markets, ideas, and capital. With urging from Jane Jacobs, the noted urbanist and writer who then sat on our board, we started to think about establishing an urban presence and program. We settled on the idea of creating a marketplace and center — a place where the emerging ideas, products, and services of the conservation economy could find a home and a growing audience.

What is a conservation economy? Call it a restorative economy, sustainability, or a civil society. All of these words describe the same ideal: An economy that prospers within the ecological limits of its region's resources and in fact restores its natural systems. This approach generates enduring prosperity, and in so doing, spreads wealth broadly, democratizing capital, and building social equity.

Native people have nurtured a conservation economy in the region for millennia, based largely on the rich abundance of salmon. Here, the Heiltsuk First Nation celebrates the repatriation of ancestral lands at the mouth of the Koeye, an important salmon river in mid-coast British Columbia.

In 1998 Ecotrust went looking for a building. We wanted an old building to help anchor us in the region's history — to take a building from the time of westward expansion (and a frontier economy) and redeploy it as a hub for the new conservation economy. We also wanted to be conveniently and centrally located to

Ecotrust's mission is to build Salmon Nation — a place where people and wild salmon thrive. Salmon Nation's geography is defined by the range of Pacific salmon.

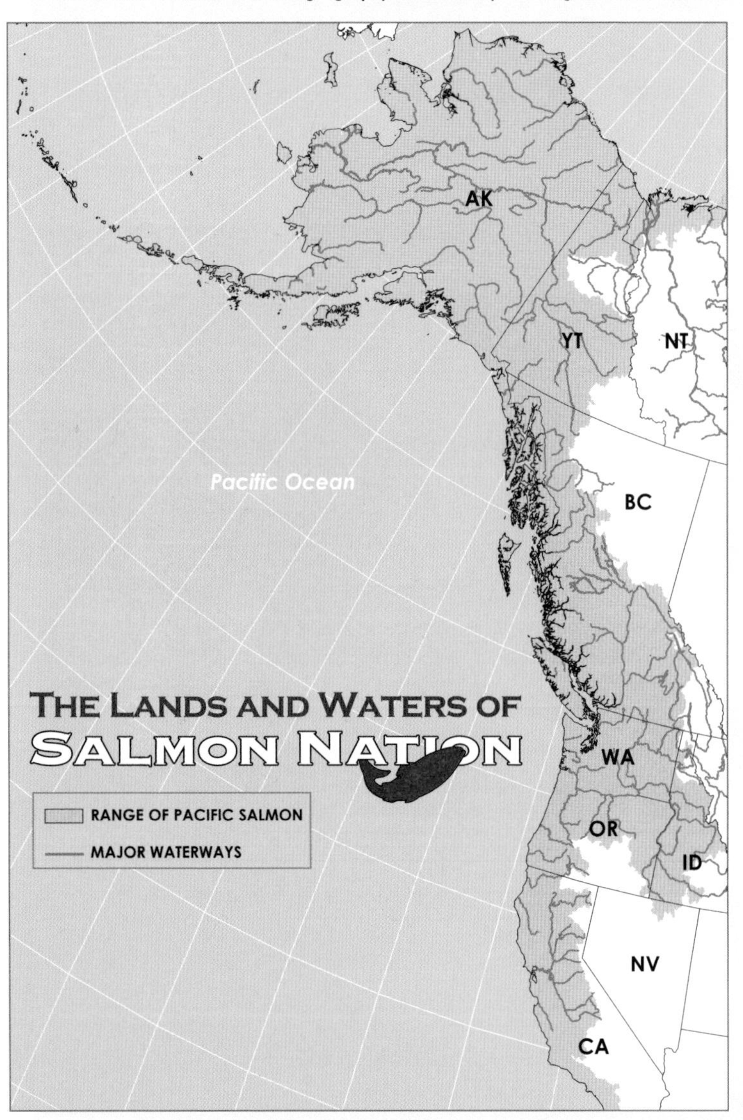

reduce transportation infrastructure and energy use, to curtail urban sprawl, to support the vitality of the city center, and to maximize the flow of people to the building so we could build a clientele for the conservation economy. Finally, we wanted a site that was big enough to house a diverse array of retailers, offices, for-profit, and non-profit organizations.

We found our building in February 1998 and, with a generous donation from Portland philanthropist and founding Ecotrust board member Jean Vollum, purchased it the following month. It was perfect. Built in 1895 by the J. McCraken Company to store building supplies, the warehouse and associated loading and parking area occupied a full city block and still served as a storehouse and studio for area businesses and artists. The building's flat roof and parapet, recessed round-arched entrance, arched window openings, stucco and brick facing, and massive appearance are all classic elements of the Richardson Romanesque style (see **History of the McCraken Warehouse** on page 40). While the exterior was in need of restoration, the building itself was structurally sound. Best of all, it was situated in the heart of Portland's emerging River District. Located north of downtown, the River District is a vibrant new mixed-use, urban neighborhood being created in an old industrial area of existing warehouse buildings and 34 acres of vacant rail yards (see **River District Redevelopment** on page 48).

By 2001, Ecotrust's team of developers, architects, designers, and green building experts had transformed our neglected warehouse into a state-of-the-art, 70,000 square foot home to a diverse array of retailers, businesses, and nonprofit organizations. Upon entering, visitors are invited to take a self-guided tour exploring every nook and cranny, learning how this historic structure was transformed into a marketplace for the conservation economy and a powerful example of green building.

Building is a very powerful event. Many of its effects are apparent: buildings shape cities and towns, influence transportation patterns, create beauty or diminish it, and influence how residents move, live, and think about their potential and opportunities. Buildings also affect the landscape in ways less immediately apparent. Their construction and operation uses vast amounts of material, energy, and water. These effects can be seen in the surrounding landscape as buildings infringe upon wild lands, as dams limit stream passage to provide for increased energy needs, and as contaminated stormwater overwhelms and pollutes waterways. The shadow of buildings can also extend across the globe, to iron ore mines in the Venezuelan Amazon for steel, to old-growth forests in coastal British Columbia for framing lumber, to the Earth's atmosphere where greenhouse gases accumulate from fossil fuels used for heating and cooling.

In the Pacific Northwest there is an additional dimension to building: the extent to which it affects the health and abundance of the region's icon, the endangered Pacific salmon. Pacific salmon, which travel from cold mountain streams to the ocean and back again to spawn and die, have shaped the geography, ecology, and culture of the Pacific Northwest since the glaciers last receded. Before Euro-American settlement, abundant runs of salmon sustained and nourished the largest population of hunter-gatherers in the world. In addition to feeding people, salmon are consumed by over 137 other species,[1] including grizzly bears and bald eagles. Their decaying carcasses left along the banks of rivers and streams release valuable nutrients to trees, contributing to the productivity and diversity of the region's rain forests. Salmon are so important to the identity of this region that we call these lands Salmon Nation. Part of the reverence for salmon is a sense that their health and well-being predicts ours. Where salmon thrive, we will thrive; where salmon perish, we will be permanently diminished. Unlike humans, salmon have few mechanisms to borrow resources from other places or future generations, so they are immediately affected by changes in their environment. Like the proverbial canary in the coal mine, salmon can tell us what lies ahead.

Salmon return to their natal streams to spawn and die, providing food to over 137 species and valuable nutrients to forests.

The recent recognition that many Pacific salmon species are threatened and endangered spurred regional interest in green building. One of the primary threats to salmon is the extent to which building creates impervious surfaces. These surfaces cause stormwater to run off sites in high-velocity pulses, scouring out stream beds and polluting surface water with silt, oil, grease, and yard chemicals picked up on the way downhill. Water running over hot pavement during summer storms can also significantly raise the temperature of streams, affecting native fish species that are adapted to the region's cold waters. With less groundwater recharge, streams dry up in the summer, creating even more hostile conditions for salmon. More effective management of stormwater is thus a central theme of green building. Salmon are also affected by other dimensions of building, including energy use (primarily hydroelectric); the forest management that yields construction lumber; and toxic substances used in construction or building materials that find their way into groundwater and streams. Green building addresses these effects through energy and water conservation, by using wood only from well-managed forests, and by eliminating or minimizing the use of toxic substances.

In the Pacific Northwest, green building generates enormous private and public benefits, illustrating the point that what is good for salmon is good for people. Private benefits include lower construction waste disposal costs, lower operating costs, lower liability due to minimizing toxic substances, and enhanced worker productivity in response to green features such as improved indoor air quality,

Green building uses wood from well-managed forests that maintain a continuous forest cover.

access to natural light, and operable windows — all of which lead to higher rates of leasing and occupancy. The public benefits of green building are even more substantial: reduced greenhouse gases, higher water quality, lower water use, reduction in toxins, improved air quality, and less pressure on natural resources, all of which help conserve biodiversity.

Despite these advantages, green building as measured by the U.S. Green Building Council, currently has only a 3% market share in new commercial development. If green building does indeed save money, produce a better building, and wins widespread admiration and recognition, wouldn't all buildings be green? While green building is compelling, there are practical and psychological barriers limiting its rapid adoption. Developers have much at stake. Buildings are very expensive propositions, with potential daily cash outflows on large projects of $1 million or more in materials and labor. Scheduling is also highly complex, with many sequential and interconnected tasks. A slip in schedule by one contractor can have consequences for the building timeline and project well beyond the scope or budget of the individual task. Finally, developers and builders have tremendous accountability and liability for building performance and safety. Developers and builders often deal with these high stakes by establishing and maintaining close relationships with a small number of trusted contractors and suppliers. The past performance of these contractors and products, and their familiarity with the builders' preferences and operations, reduces risk and time in sourcing materials and services.

Green building, with its new array of approaches, products and services, presents obvious and immediate challenges. It entails replacing some comfortable, proven relationships and products with untested and unfamiliar new products and suppliers. It also involves finding time for evaluation just when the builder is consumed with the building schedule and inevitable crises. Unless a builder has a deep personal commitment to environmental stewardship, the introduction to green building usually comes as a regulatory requirement or owner mandate. Yet, no matter the difficulty of adoption, when people go through the green building process, the conversion is usually swift and permanent. Once comfort is established and the green building benefits begin to flow, everyone involved is generally convinced and applies green building approaches to all subsequent projects. Owners, developers, architects, builders, and contractors report that green building is simply more fun, more satisfying, and more stimulating. It provides an additional dimension to building beyond budget, design, and performance, one that connects the act of building firmly and profoundly to its community and landscape.

Rob Bennett, manager of the City of Portland's Green Building Division and Stuart Cowan, a sustainability and green building consultant, explore these themes in Chapter 2, "The Case for Green Building." They pay special attention to the perennial question of whether green building construction costs more and the extent to which higher construction costs are offset by reductions in operating expenses. They also discuss the role green building can play in economic development, yielding multiple economic, social, and environmental benefits, including the stimulation of new markets and products that can help in the transition to a conservation economy. The authors also describe the role the City of Portland has played in catalyzing green building in the region, from incentive funds to technical resources and city mandates for green public buildings.

As interest in green building has grown, so has the need for a systematic way to describe, measure, and report on the environmental effects and features of buildings. In Chapter 3, green building consultant and architect Ralph DiNola describes the Leadership in Energy and Environmental Design (LEED™) program, developed by the U.S. Green Building Council. LEED is a flexible rating system that serves as an evaluation tool and as a checklist to guide building decisions. DiNola describes the evolution and current status of LEED, explains how the system works, and discusses highlights of the Natural Capital Center's LEED score.

The view from the Natural Capital Center's terrace of the neighborhood's mix of redeveloped warehouses and new construction, with Forest Park in the background.

Redeveloping historic buildings such as the Natural Capital Center is unfortunately not as easy and financially rewarding a choice as green building. Historic buildings are often limited by their structure, size, and orientation, which may no longer be in keeping with surrounding land uses. In addition, old buildings are often full of surprises that can substantially increase the budget and lengthen the construction schedule. Portland developer Bob Naito, who has been involved in numerous historic redevelopments in Portland and beyond, including the Natural Capital Center, describes the opportunities and challenges of historic building redevelopment in Chapter 4. He relates some of the tools and resources available for redevelopment, primarily the 20% historic rehabilitation tax credit, and how redevelopment projects can qualify for this credit. Naito also tells the story of the McCraken warehouse's transformation into the Natural Capital Center and the factors that favored its preservation while historic buildings nearby fell to the wrecking ball.

In Chapter 5, Ecotrust project manager Bettina von Hagen and Bob Naito recount the highlights of the Natural Capital Center redevelopment from the purchase of the building in 1998 through its occupancy in September 2001. They detail the owner's objectives and the process of translating these broad goals into a building

The loading dock at the Natural Capital Center, bordered by plantings of fruits and herbs, provides a place to relax and enjoy the outdoors.

program and plans. They touch on the main construction elements, describe setbacks, and lay out the construction budget and financing sources.

The next three chapters elaborate on the key areas of opportunity for conservation in any green building project — energy, water, and materials. In Chapter 6, Mike O'Brien, a green building specialist for the City of Portland's Green Building Division, Erin Kellogg, and Bob Naito make a powerful argument for energy conservation and describe the energy strategies employed in the Natural Capital Center, including those that were considered but not used. The authors offer a new paradigm for thinking about energy conservation in buildings that goes well beyond light bulbs and solar energy.

Located in the heart of the country's rainiest region, Portland is forced to address the challenges — and opportunities — of designing buildings with water in mind. In Chapter 7, Eugénie Frerichs, project coordinator for the Natural Capital Center's ecoroof planting design and installation, explains how history has taught us that working with water in buildings is far more effective than fighting it. The chapter challenges the building community to shift site design towards using water as a material akin to bricks and mortar, and offers profiles of three solutions at varying scales that foreshadow emerging trends in water conservation and stormwater management.

In Chapter 8, Bettina von Hagen describes how, faced with a daunting array of choices, the building team developed a set of criteria based on Ecotrust's values, mission, and regional context to guide decisions about which materials to use in the Natural Capital Center. She then shows the promise that new, sophisticated, life-cycle analysis tools hold for delivering more definitive answers to materials-related questions.

All the green strategies in the world will not produce a building that functions as gracefully as a natural ecosystem, if the space does not engage and inspire. In the concluding chapter, Eugénie Frerichs describes how Ecotrust designed the Natural Capital Center to create a sense of community within and without its walls, and evaluates how those working in this innovative space have reacted to it, and forged bonds with each other and the neighborhood.

Each of the chapters contain several sidebars that furnish more detail about significant points raised in the text, as well as photographs of the redevelopment, and a diagram illustrating important features of the building relevant to that chapter. Appendices offer notes for each chapter, biographies of the contributors, and profiles of the sponsoring organizations.

Ecotrust hoped that the Natural Capital Center would spark the imagination and creativity of those who work in and visit the building. What we did not fully anticipate was the degree to which we would become addicted to green building in the process. In addition to adding a significant element of fun and fascination to the project, we discovered that "going green" simply made good sense. It did not cost significantly more than conventional building techniques, and is making a world of difference in the building's ecological impact and the health and productivity of its occupants. It is our wish that the story of the Natural Capital Center's redevelopment and transformation will persuade others that the only way to build — and rebuild — is green. ■

WELCOME

by Stuart Cowan and Rob Bennett

Winston Churchill once declared that, "We shape our buildings; thereafter they shape us." Buildings, streetscapes, infrastructure, and other elements of the built environment have an enormous impact on our daily experience, our economies, and our cultures. Well-conceived buildings enhance health and productivity, while poorly-conceived buildings can cause both illness and diminished communities. Buildings have the power to activate the districts around them, bringing new energy to the streets and stimulating investment. The livability, prosperity, and identity of a region ultimately depend on the steady unfolding of building decisions — what is neglected and what revitalized; what land is built on and what spared; who will use the structure, and for what purpose. Indeed, such decisions are critical to communities' ability to adapt to change and ultimately prosper over time through the growth of dynamic neighborhoods and vital cityscapes.

Harnessing the Built Environment

In their important book *The Regional City*, planners Peter Calthorpe and William Fulton argue that even in a globalizing economy, competitiveness ultimately depends on the geometry, mix of land uses, and infrastructure of the built environment. They advocate channeling new development into existing centers and along transit lines while greatly expanding networks of protected open space. Calthorpe's firm played a key role in developing Portland Metro's 2040 Framework Plan, which accomplishes this by designating a hierarchy of centers including the central city, six regional centers, and numerous town centers and transit oriented developments. Other cities like Salt Lake City and Chicago are following suit with similar plans. Combined with careful attention to balancing jobs and housing, and to providing a diversity of housing types, this approach to regional development can enhance social equity and strengthen economic networks.[1]

The Natural Capital Center provides a good example of how to apply these ideas at the site level. Situated at the edge of the River District, it is surrounded by several blocks of recent mixed-use developments, typically containing dense housing above a first floor of galleries, restaurants, stores, and offices. A new streetcar line stops at the building, linking it to nearby neighborhoods and downtown.

The Portland Streetcar, which stops directly in front of the Natural Capital Center, connects the River District to downtown Portland.

THE ECOLOGICAL IMPACT OF BUILDINGS

In the United States, 36% of all energy consumption and 36% of all carbon dioxide emissions are directly or indirectly related to buildings and their construction.[2] With off-the-shelf and economically viable energy efficiency technologies and design strategies, new construction and retrofits could easily achieve 20% greater energy efficiency. This would reduce total U.S. carbon dioxide emissions by 7%, or 110 million metric tons. About 20% to 30% of landfill space is taken up by construction and demolition debris, much of which could have been recycled. Over 136 million tons of construction and demolition waste is generated in the U.S. annually, and only 20-30% of that waste is recovered.[3]

At least 30% of new and renovated buildings suffer from poor indoor air quality as a result of toxic emissions, off gassing, and pathogens related to inadequate moisture protection and insufficient fresh air ventilation.[4] With Americans spending an average of 90% of their time indoors, the U.S. Environmental Protection Agency estimates lost productivity from Sick Building Syndrome at $60 billion annually.

Globally, buildings use 25% of all forest products, 10% of freshwater withdrawals, and 40% of material and energy flows.[5] To place this in local perspective, a standard wood-framed home consumes over one acre of forest. At the Portland metro area's current rate of homebuilding, this is equivalent to cutting almost three-quarters of Forest Park — the largest green belt in any city in the country — annually. ■

HISTORICALLY, BUILDINGS HAVE USED...

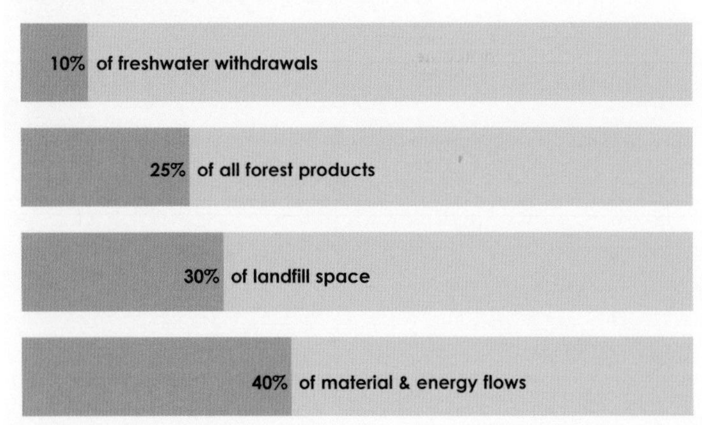

Several bus lines and the City's rail station are within four blocks, and light rail is within a half mile. The renovation of the Natural Capital Center reflects the history of the district — echoing the brickwork, windows, and other features of nearby structures — while allowing the building to gracefully adapt to the functions of a twenty-first century mixed-use commercial building.

The built environment reflects and embodies the values underlying its construction. It is as critical to the identity of a nation as its political, economic, and cultural institutions. An Italian hill town, a Japanese teahouse, a pueblo adobe dwelling, or a New England commons share a profound sense of place. Each demonstrates the possibility of weaving climate and season, topography and vegetation, casual interaction and formal ritual into the structure, materials, and program of a building. The materials and design of the Natural Capital Center, for example, tie it to its regional identity as a building within Salmon Nation: Douglas-fir timbers and century-old brick shape its shell, it is permeable to natural light, its site is landscaped with native plants, it welcomes rain back into the soil, provides multiple gathering places, and is designed to cultivate a sense of community.

Building the Case

In the United States, the costs of sprawl have become overwhelmingly clear, with dozens of cities and states passing recent legislation favoring enhanced transit access (e.g. light rail in Dallas), urban growth boundaries (e.g. San Jose), and statewide open space planning (e.g. wildlands networks in Florida). The values that shaped sprawl — automobile access, abundant land, strict separation of uses, and disposable buildings — are slowly shifting. We are finally starting to see buildings, communities, and ecosystems in an integrated way, just as indigenous cultures have for thousands of years.

Recent studies show that denser, mixed-use development with good transit access significantly reduces energy use for both transportation (through the shift to public transit, walking, biking, and shorter commutes) and heating and cooling (by decreased size of housing units).[6] When coordinated regionally, this clustered development form can also preserve significant green spaces while maintaining working farms, ranches, and forests near city limits. Ironically, these ideas actually hark back to the golden age of modern town planning in the United States and Europe, between 1900 and 1930. During this time cities like Stockholm and Copenhagen adopted visionary regional plans concentrating development along commuter rail corridors while American cities like Portland and Los Angeles sprouted "streetcar suburbs."

The **ecological footprint** of a building, a concept developed by William Rees at the University of British Columbia, is generally much larger than the building's actual footprint. Rees compares the amount of energy and materials consumed by the building to the actual land area required to produce them. Converting this into a numerical calculation enables him to assess the relative ecological impact of individual buidlings, a neighborhood, or even an entire country. The term is now commonly used in the green building industry and beyond as a unit of measurement.

The twenty-first century equivalent adds a critical new element: green building practices. Green building emphasizes both occupant health and a decreased **ecological footprint**. A hundred years ago, houses had lead piping, lead paint, poor insulation, single glazed windows, unreinforced masonry walls, drafts, improper ventilation, dangerous fireplaces, and old-growth wood. Today's green building strategies include brownfield redevelopment, siting buildings near existing transit, managing stormwater naturally on site, carefully recycling and reusing construction waste, using low toxic materials, harvesting daylight and natural ventilation, and other environmentally sound design and construction practices. In addition, green buildings like the Natural Capital Center play a pivotal role in a sustainable economic development strategy because of their enormous triple bottom line benefits:

Economic Returns

Green buildings are excellent investments. Their initial cost may be slightly higher, perhaps by 1–6%, but their reduced consumption of energy and water, decreased maintenance costs, extended lifespan, and enhanced worker productivity provide a quick payback (see Green Building Economics on page 22). Studies show that green buildings increase in value more rapidly than comparable conventional buildings, attract and retain tenants more effectively, cost less to operate and maintain, and hold their value for longer periods.[7]

Environmental Returns

Green buildings form a new kind of ecological infrastructure for a city. They have the potential to gather most or all of their own water and energy. They use solar orientation strategies to downsize Heating Ventilation and Cooling Systems (HVAC systems). Green buildings can treat most or all of their own stormwater and wastewater. They are designed with a smaller footprint and sited to minimize habitat disruption and sometimes even enhance biodiversity. Green buildings emphasize non-toxic, regional, and sustainably harvested materials. They attempt to offer high levels of fresh air exchange and advanced thermal comfort.

Located at the mouth of the Columbia River, Mill Pond village exemplifies brownfield redevelopment at work. Ecotrust partner Shorebank Enterprise Pacific worked with the City of Astoria and the Department of Environmental Quality to clean up and transform this highly contaminated 16-acre mill site into a mixed-use, pedestrian friendly green development, and ShoreBank Pacific provided financing to the developer.

OPPORTUNITIES IN GREEN BUILDING

A sampling of industries with potential for growth:

Architecture
- Daylighting, passive solar design, water capture and reuse

Planning
- Transportation options: Car sharing programs, bicycles, public transit programs

Engineering
- Natural ventilation and energy modeling

Construction
- Energy: Photovoltaic panels, fuel cells
- Roofing: Non-toxic membranes and green roofs
- Drywall/sheetrock: High recycled content, fly ash
- Concrete: Waste fly ash, heat island reduction, permeable pavers and asphalt
- Plumbing: Water conservation fixtures
- Certified forestry: Structural building materials, floors, interior walls
- Deconstruction specialists
- Construction waste recovery
- Insulation: Non-toxic, recycled content
- Waste materials: Recycled plastic as lumber, straw bale construction
- Windows and doors: high-performance, energy-efficient products

Interior Design
- Interior finish products: Low VOC paints, glues, sealants
- Flooring/carpeting products: Non-toxic and recyclable/ recycled
- Certified forestry: Finishes, veneers, cupboards and countertops, furniture
- Lighting: Energy efficient fixtures, smart controls

Landscape Architecture
- Horticulture: Native plants
- Bioswales
- Landscaping maintenance: Non-toxic, drip irrigation systems

Real Estate Management
- Cleaning products
- Community development

Real Estate Development
- Green real estate development

Retail Stores
- Environmental building products
- Salvaged building products ■

Environmental Building Supplies in southeast Portland has been selling natural, low-toxic and rapidly renewable building materials since 1993. www.ecohaus.com

Social Returns

Green buildings are healthy places to live and work, conducive to rich interactions, and are well-integrated into pedestrian and transit-friendly neighborhoods. At their best, they are great architecture — providing a deep sense of historical and ecological continuity. Green buildings reinforce people's connection to natural systems — celebrating the interface of the built and natural worlds.

The range and magnitude of the environmental and social impacts of buildings is extraordinary. Building materials have consequences throughout their entire life-cycles, including extraction, manufacturing and processing, transportation, construction, maintenance, demolition or deconstruction, and reuse. Typically, building operations and maintenance (including heating, cooling, lighting, and water use) are even more detrimental to the environment than materials when evaluated over the building's lifetime. Indoor air quality, lighting, interior design, and streetscapes profoundly influence the health and productivity of building occupants (See The Ecological Impact of Buildings on page 18).

Conventional buildings are the outcome of a flawed design process. They flow from a system of accounting that fails to integrate capital budgets and operations budgets; from a system of prices that does not reflect ecological and social costs; and from a system of knowledge that splits nature from culture. Green building represents a conscious effort to use a modified set of assumptions for designing and constructing buildings. Building green begins by acknowledging a responsibility to the community and to the environment.

Green building also means asking where materials come from and what the impact of their extraction, processing, transport, installation, and future deconstruction will have on the environment, on workers, and on occupants and communities. Green building includes looking past short-term expediency to long-term costs and benefits that incorporate the true life-cycle costs of construction and material decisions. (For a fuller discussion of life-cycle costs analysis, see Chapter 8.)

Green building results in safer, healthier, and more productive workers and building occupants. Green building prepares for the future while serving the present. Increasingly, green building also provides cachet for a project, lending it momentum and credibility.

Green Building as an Economic Development Strategy

The green building sector holds considerable promise as part of the broader market shift to a conservation economy. It encompasses a wide variety of professional services: architecture, planning, engineering, construction, landscape architecture, interior design, real estate management and development, and others. It also includes innovative green building products like sustainably harvested wood, fiber materials (e.g. straw bale or compressed straw panels), fly ash cement, non-toxic paints and finishes, low-flow plumbing fixtures, photovoltaic panels, and fuel cells. Advanced sorting and materials recovery practices during building construction and deconstruction also create the feedstock for many specialized recycling and remanufacturing facilities.

A growing body of data reveals that sustainable building products can be more profitable than conventional products. Many of the typical investments — for instance in energy-efficient lighting, native landscaping, transportation demand management, and pollution prevention — offer a direct payback time of under three years.[8] Other investments require the evaluation and internalization of social and environmental costs over a project's entire life cycle. This internal use of true cost pricing allows green businesses to seize a leadership role, beating others to market.

Portland-based Rejuvenation, Inc. provides a good example of the greening of building products. As the country's largest producer of period lighting, Rejuvenation employs a unique antiquing process to give its fixtures the right look for the marketplace — a process that used to discharge over 30,000 gallons of selenium-tainted wastewater a year. Selenium is a known bioaccumulator harmful to human and watershed health. Rejuvenation developed an alternative processing system that eliminated the use of water and the discharge of selenium. In addition to the environmental benefits, this resulted in over $21,000 in annual savings due to decreased utility, permitting, and operation costs.

Another example of a business working to create this market shift is The ReBuilding Center. Also based in Portland, the company sells a wide range of quality salvaged building materials in a 62,000 square foot warehouse space. The Center acquires materials from donations and the work of its skilled deconstruction crews, which have carefully dismantled dozens of residences as well as large institutional buildings, and even a large grain mill. The Center is able to divert millions of pounds of reusable building and remodeling materials from the waste stream, provide quality materials to people of all income levels, and employ dozens of people.

The ReBuilding Center in north Portland carefully deconstructs and salvages building materials to sell for re-use at an affordable price.

Returns on Investment

As green building practices become more commonplace, the economic and human performance benefits are becoming apparent. Here are some typical results for green building projects:[9]

▲ Prairie Crossing
Grayslake, Illinois
Residential community near Chicago saved $1.4 million on infrastructure costs by using natural stormwater drainage and narrower streets; homes use 50% less energy for heating and cooling.

▲ Selma Middle School
Johnston County, North Carolina
School students who transferred to a day lit school outperformed those at the older school on achievement tests by 5% the first year and 14% after three years. Those who transferred to another school without day lighting did not show the improvement. Day lighting also helped reduce operations costs by an average of $0.25 per square foot or $25,000 per year.

▲ Village Homes
Davis, California
Residential community with homes selling for $10 to $25 per square foot more than comparable homes in the area; special construction reduced energy use 33% to 50% ; reduced paving decreased local air temperature by 15°.

▲ Herman Miller Greenhouse
Holland, Michigan
Industrial building has reduced water and sewer costs by 65%; high employee satisfaction and retention.

▲ C.K. Choi Building
University of British Columbia, Vancouver, BC
Electrical savings of $15,000 or 190,000 kilowatts per year; composting toilets save 1,000 to 1,500 gallons of water per day.

▲ Audubon House
New York, New York
Saved 27% over new construction by reusing historic building; energy consumption down by two-thirds.

Savings

Estimated Resource Savings in Portland Buildings

The City of Portland Green Building Program set an aggressive goal for its first two years: adopting green practices in 600 units of housing and three million square feet of government, commercial, and mixed-use space. The expected annual resource savings from achieving this goal are as follows:

$4 million in increased employee productivity	Studies have found productivity increases of 6–15% due to lighting, ventilation, and other green features.[10] This projection assumes a very modest gain of 2%.
8 million gallons of water saved	Assumes a 10% reduction in water consumption over standard practice.
5 million kilowatt-hours of electricity saved	Based on a 10% reduction in energy consumption over Oregon Energy Code for residential construction and commercial renovations, and a 15% reduction for new commercial construction.
170,000 therms of natural gas saved	Based on a 10% reduction in energy consumption over Oregon Energy Code for residential construction and commercial renovations, and a 15% reduction for new commercial construction.
$450,000 in utility bill savings	Based on current electric, natural gas, and water rates.
30 million gallons of stormwater managed beyond City standards	Assumes the use of innovative stormwater treatment techniques that not only keep water out of the combined-sewer overflow system, but also recharge groundwater, allow more evapotranspiration, and lead to cleaner, cooler water.
3,400 metric tons of CO_2 reduced	Based on energy saving assumptions above.

Building tours continue to be well-attended long after the building opening.

SHOREBANK PACIFIC'S NEW GREEN HEADQUARTERS

While the Natural Capital Center was being redeveloped, another green building was taking shape 100 miles downriver at the mouth of the Columbia in the fishing town of Ilwaco, Washington. The building was to serve as permanent headquarters for the ShoreBank Pacific Companies, affiliates of Ecotrust, that provide financing, technical assistance and support to businesses and initiatives that are working to improve economic, environmental, and social conditions in coastal communities of Oregon and Washington. After five years of investment in the community, including over $50 million in loans to over 200 businesses, the ShoreBank Pacific Companies wanted to create a permanent home that would reflect its confidence and optimism in the future for coastal communities. The effort was led by John Berdes, who manages ShoreBank Enterprise Pacific, the non-profit affiliate of ShoreBank Pacific. Berdes was also involved in the early development phases of the Natural Capital Center.

Berdes secured the services of local architect and builder Erik Fagerland to design and build the 8,500 square foot, three story, wood-frame structure. The site itself, located in the Port of Ilwaco, was a previously contaminated gas station. The building team prioritized design and construction features that would inspire replication by others in the rural community. Salvaged posts and beams from an industrial warehouse in the nearby Port of Astoria (Oregon) were used for structural components, and remilled salvaged lumber was used throughout the building. Through careful orientation and strategic placement of windows, the building is cooled through natural ventilation. Heating is provided by a hydronic heating system in the floor and by passive solar. Stormwater is captured and infiltrates through bioswales and permeable paving. ShoreBank's $1.1 million ($110/SF) project also had its intended impact in the redevelopment of the Port area; since it was completed in 2001 there has been a multi-million dollar public and private reinvestment by their neighbors and the Port district itself.

The ShoreBank Pacific headquarters have inspired a flurry of green building in the area and the formation of a local Green Building Council, demonstrating once again the infectious nature of green building and the power of example. ■

— John Berdes, Shorebank Enterprise Pacific

In California's Central Valley, waste wheat straw and rice straw used to be burned in the fields, reducing air quality, causing respiratory illnesses, and diminishing visibility up to a hundred miles away. With recent regulations banning this practice, these former waste products have become increasingly popular as building materials. A standard straw bale wall insulation system achieves about R-40, twice what energy codes require.[11] In several states, building codes have been developed for these materials, making their use routine. Wheat straw can also be compressed into insulated panels and plywood-like boards.

Waste fly ash from coal-fired utilities is now being added to concrete, creating a new fly ash concrete which is structurally stronger and lighter in weight than conventional concrete. The Green Building Program for the City of Austin, Texas estimates that 30% of all fly ash in the United States is presently diverted to fly ash concrete for use in wall-form products and other applications. This product offers superior performance without any cost premium.

To stimulate market transformation that ultimately reduces the direct and indirect societal costs of development, financiers, appraisers, code officials, planners, economic development professionals, and others must become active partners. Together they can create incentives and regulatory tools that encourage the green building sector to thrive. With new technologies and practices, financial incentives, and supportive building and land code regulations, developers will begin systematically to use green building practices. What is now a niche market will become standard practice and a new cycle of increasingly efficient and safe practices will then be within reach.

Encouraging Green Building

Luckily, throughout the United States this type of leadership is beginning to emerge. Portland's developers, designers, and building professionals are at the vanguard of this movement, finding creative new ways of building. In addition to the Natural Capital Center, several projects scattered across the city — the Brewery Blocks, Buckman Heights, Museum South Apartments, and Viridian Place — demonstrate that the benefits of green building practices are compelling.

To accelerate the growth of the green building sector throughout Portland the City partnered with other public and private sector organizations, and together launched the innovative and nationally recognized Green Building Initiative in 1999. With the leadership of City Commissioner Dan Saltzman, the Initiative gained momentum and status through several key policy decisions. First, Portland City Council granted it official status as a City program — the Green Building Division (G/Rated) in the Office of Sustainable Development (OSD). To give the program greater leverage, the Council then passed the City of Portland Green Building Policy stipulating that all city facilities, infrastructure, and city-funded projects be built and retrofit using healthy and resource efficient building practices. The Portland Development Commission (PDC), another major capital works agency in the city, shortly followed suit, passing a groundbreaking policy requiring all new PDC-financed development to incorporate green building measures.

The policy framework firmly in place, G/Rated quickly developed a multi-faceted green building program, providing technical assistance and compiling related resources and information. It targeted the building industry with key publications including a 100-page resource guide, *Greening Portland's Affordable Housing,* which establishes goals and practical, cost-effective strategies to increase the environmental performance and durability of all of Portland's subsidized housing; followed by the nation's first resource guide for greening commercial remodels, *Creating a High Performance Workspace*. This guide offers expert advice on lighting, energy efficiency, indoor air quality, and waste reduction to those moving an organization into a new or retrofitted commercial space. Both publications include important, practical information like project checklists, model specifications, and lists of regional product vendors and manufacturers. To provide more tangible, hands-on demonstrations of green building practices, G/Rated sponsors an annual *Build it Green* tour of homes. The first tour, held in 2002, featured 15 residential homes in Portland to a sold-out audience. Given the positive response to these initiatives, G/Rated launched *ReThink: Innovation in Ecological Design and Construction,* a sixteen-week, comprehensive green building training series for commercial and residential building design and construction professionals.

In July 2000, Commissioner Saltzman and OSD convened a citizen committee to provide input on how to structure an incentive program to stimulate demand for green building from businesses, commercial developers, and homebuilders. Subsequently, OSD established a Green Investment Fund to provide financial incentive for commercial, residential, subsidized housing, and emerging green building technologies projects. A one-time $700,000 allocation from the Solid Waste and Recycling Reserve Fund and another $100,000 from OSD's fiscal year 2001-2002 budget, brought the total Green Investment Fund to $800,000 to be spent between 2000 and 2002. As a powerful non-monetary incentive, Portland also established a local version of the national LEED green building standard. The

The Brewery Blocks, a five-block project in northwest Portland, uses several green building strategies, including green roofs, solar photovoltaic panels, energy efficiency, and renovation and reuse of much of the Weinhard Brewhouse's original 1860s brick construction.

GREEN BUILDING IN SEATTLE

The City of Seattle's biggest capital improvement program since the Seattle fire of 1889 launched the largest publicly funded LEED construction program in the world. Inspired by the City of Seattle Sustainable Building Policy, adopted by unanimous Council resolution in February 2000, the City now has 14 major capital construction projects expected to meet or exceed the LEED Silver standard. Projects include the new City Hall, Justice Center, and Central Library. The vision is that all future City capital design, construction, and operations will be done sustainably, so that the City can consider its buildings a Sustainable Capital Investment Portfolio, with investments that yield profits over time. Preliminary calculations show that the City's 14 planned LEED projects will save over $800,000 in annual operating costs. This does not include the expected benefits to staff and visitors. The average incremental cost is about 2.4% over conventional design and construction costs. Leading by example, the City is accelerating sustainable building in private sector development. ■

The new 200,000 square foot Seattle City Hall meets the LEED Silver rating standard. The building maximizes natural light and views, harvests rainwater for toilet flushing and site irrigation, has a green roof on the second floor, includes a large proportion of recycled-content materials, and is designed to endure for a hundred years.

first such local adaptation of LEED approved by the U.S. Green Building Council, Portland LEED tailors the national standard to local building and development requirements, while maintaining third party verification and official certification by the USGBC. G/Rated provides technical support to local projects trying to attain this prestigious award for green performance.

Across the country, other municipalities and state and federal agencies are encouraging green building practices through similar incentives and assistance programs. The City of Austin, Texas has been encouraging this sector since 1991, adopting the country's first green building guidelines for residential construction. Boulder, Colorado; Seattle, Washington; Santa Monica and San Diego, California; and an assortment of federal and state agencies, now require their facilities to be LEED certified. Incentives are also being crafted to encourage private sector green development. In addition to Portland's Green Investment Fund, Seattle has developed a cash incentive program, Arlington County, Virginia has created a density bonus, and Santa Barbara, California an expedited permitting incentive.

In Portland, the mix of policy, incentives, and technical assistance seems to be working. As of February 2003, 41 commercial and mixed-use buildings, totaling 3.1 million square feet, had incorporated green building design and construction practices. The Green Investment Fund and the PDC's affordable housing requirements added another 1,314 units of efficient, durable, healthy housing to this mix. More than 30 subsidized and market-rate housing projects with almost 2,000 units are in the pipeline now. As of July 2003, 36 LEED projects were registered in the Portland metro region, the highest such concentration in North America. The Oregon Office of Energy has developed a Business Energy Tax Credit, known as the BETC, to complement Portland LEED, and the local utility, Portland General Electric, has launched an aggressive green building program for commercial and residential development and started a for-profit, green building consulting firm (see **Stimulating Green Building Through Tax Credits** on page 72).

Conclusion

The Natural Capital Center benefited from many of these programs. The initial LEED certification was partially funded by the City of Portland's Green Investment Fund, which provided $20,000 to projects seeking LEED certification at the silver level or higher (see Chapter 3 for description of LEED levels). The City's Bureau of Environmental Services provided a $75,000 grant to finance the difference in cost between a standard roof and an ecoroof as part of a program to catalyze the use of ecoroofs in Portland. Finally, the Natural Capital Center obtained a Business Energy Tax Credit provided by the Office of Energy for LEED-certified projects. Together these programs contributed approximately $200,000 to help fund LEED certification and green features that added significant public benefits to the project. The Green Investment Fund has turned out to be a cornerstone in the acceleration of green building practices in Portland. To date it has helped to support 28 commercial building projects totaling over 1.5 million square feet; 35 residential projects representing a range of housing types including two multi-family affordable housing projects totaling 278 housing units; and 13 projects implementing a range of emerging green technologies. Together, these projects are beginning to achieve the resource savings targets set out by the Green Building Program (see **Green Building Economics** on page 22).

Local firms are also reorganizing and training their staffs to position their businesses to take advantage of the growing demand for green buildings. Companies that supply green building products like Environmental Building Supplies, Stormwater Management, Inc., Timber Tek, The ReBuilding Center, and Rejuvenation continue to grow. This trend will continue as companies, service providers, and developers begin to see the many benefits of green development.

Green building may seem to add daunting complexity to a project. Yet as Ecotrust and others have found, green building not only makes tremendous economic sense for the owner, but also stimulates new industries, strengthens economies, and enhances a region's livability and identity. ■

SETTING THE STANDARD

by Ralph DiNola

As more and more people realize that green building makes sense, experimentation with green technology has begun to grow exponentially. Some projects, like Ecotrust's Natural Capital Center, do a wholesale evaluation and employ a wide range of green strategies. Others take a more incremental approach, tackling one issue at a time, such as energy or water conservation or transportation options. Yet, how does the building team know — particularly if a project takes a wholesale approach to green building — that when the last nails are pounded and the low-energy lights switched on, that it has achieved the environmental returns anticipated at the design stage?

Ecotrust, like a growing number of owners and operators, turned to a third party — the U.S. Green Building Council's Leadership in Energy and Environmental Design (LEED™) program — to verify the environmental performance of its building. LEED is the national standard for green building design and construction and the Natural Capital Center is the first historic building in the United States to receive LEED's prestigious Gold certification.

Why Certify?

Why certify? The best way to answer this question is to look at successful certification systems in different industries for comparison. Two good examples are certified organic food and Forest Stewardship Council (FSC) certified wood.

As a consumer, would you feel confident if your lumber distributor told you, "This wood comes from a sustainable forest," without seeing a chain-of-custody certificate explaining exactly where it originated and how that forest is managed? Would you accept a statement from your grocer that, "No pesticides were detected on this produce," without third party verification? These questions capture the motivation behind the certification movement. A consumer purchasing FSC certified wood is assured that each piece of lumber comes from a forest managed in accordance with FSC requirements, that include land tenure, workers' rights, and a responsible management plan that ensures the long term health of the forest ecosystem. When a consumer buys certified organic food, the cus-

DESIGN CHARETTE: ESTABLISHING THE VISION AND THE GOALS

The design charette is a collaborative, facilitated brainstorming process that may range from a few hours to several days in length. It usually involves the building owner and design team, but may also include the general contractor and tenant representatives. During the charette, participants create goals for environmental stewardship and energy efficiency and then identify strategies to accomplish those goals. Neutral facilitators with professional experience in design and construction pose key questions from a fresh perspective to inspire discussion and elicit the expertise of individuals in the room. By managing the charette process and dialogue, the facilitators enable the participants to focus on the content — the project's environmental and energy goals, strategies for success, and available resources. The process generates a supportive atmosphere where all parties take ownership in the sustainable design elements of the project. It offers the ideal venue for capitalizing on the combined knowledge of the team members and forging effective working relationships.

Author and green building consultant Ralph DiNola leads a design charette with a LEED project design team.

The typical design charette will deliver the following results:

- A preliminary assessment for LEED certification
- A list of a project's energy and environmental goals
- An outline of the green building strategy for the project
- An initial team-building experience
- A greater team understanding of the various aspects and values of green building ■

tomer is assured that a third party authority has verified that the food was grown in accordance with the requirements of the standards of an organization such as Oregon Tilth or Quality Assurance International (QAI). These requirements include that the produce be grown without chemical fertilizers or pesticides. In a similar way, LEED certification provides assurance that a building has complied with an established set of standards for green building.

The Emergence of LEED

Even as interest in the industry grew, for many years there was little agreement on the definition of "green buildings" in North America. With the best of intentions, many developers incorporated a single environmental improvement or incremental approach in their projects and declared them "green." With no formal standards, the term had little substance. People in the industry also had specific concerns about energy and water conservation, limited natural resources and habitat, solid waste, and worker health and productivity.

The non-profit U.S. Green Building Council (USGBC), formed in 1993, became the first industry association to identify building measures that would address these concerns. In 1998, the Council developed LEED as an independent green building rating system and released the LEED 2.0 Green Building Rating System in 2000. Created through consensus by a group of volunteer professionals from a wide cross-section of the design and construction industry, LEED was intended to:

- Offer design guidelines
- Recognize leaders
- Stimulate green competition
- Establish market value with a recognizable national brand
- Raise consumer awareness
- Transform the marketplace

LEED now provides a framework that defines a "green building" and brings a verifiable process to building design and construction. A committee of volunteer industry professionals updates the program every few years to reflect new building technologies and ideas. The rating system is a balance among current best practices, existing proven technologies and standards, and emerging ideas and technologies. This allows a project to meet the requirements, while encouraging creative solutions and innovation. LEED also offers a common vocabulary for describing green building measures. Each time the LEED rating system is used, the terminology and standards become more prevalent in the industry, making it easier for professionals to discuss measures and technologies that achieve these criteria.

In a short period of time, LEED has gained a high degree of credibility and influence due largely to two key attributes of the program:

1. It fosters a *performance-based* approach rather than a prescriptive one. A prescriptive methodology tells the design team exactly what to implement; a performance-based methodology sets a goal and allows the design team to decide how to reach it. This encourages new ideas, generates creative strategies, and advances the development of new technologies.
2. It takes a *holistic approach* to a building's environmental performance. The system was crafted to inspire a coordinated approach to design, systems integration, and construction. This whole-building perspective explores potential synergies and connections among green measures, and can greatly reduce the cost of construction and/or operation.

How LEED Works

LEED is organized as a point-based system of prerequisites and credits and offers a scale for certification. A project can achieve LEED Certified, Silver, Gold, or Platinum. A project receives certification after earning seven prerequisites and a certain number of points from a checklist. Certification involves a three-part procedure. First, a member of the project team registers the project with the USGBC, preferably at its inception. Then, using an integrated design process during which members of the design team work together to optimize the resource and energy efficiency of the building — often beginning with a design charette (see Design Charette on page 30) — the team develops and incorporates green building strategies into the project. Once the building is operational, the team submits extensive documentation on its green features and their performance to date, and the USGBC reviews and rates the project.

The key to success in most of these projects is committing to green building before any other decisions are made. When identified early in the design process, green building strategies can be incorporated at a lower cost. The holistic design approach creates an overlap of systems and strategies, which often reduces or eliminates systems. This lowers construction and future operating costs. By comparison,

The Language of Certification[1]

The term **certified** is widely used to differentiate products and services in the marketplace, but the rigor of the standards and procedures that stand behind the term vary significantly. Generally, certification methods can be divided into three categories: first-, second-, and third-party certifications. First-party is also known as "self-certification" because the certification involves no external verification of claims. Second-party certification is achieved by participating in an affiliated organization or group — such as a trade association — that in turn asserts qualitative claims about a product or service. Third-party is the only truly "independent" certification method and consists of three primary components: 1) established standards for management and performance; 2) accredited auditors and procedures; 3) specific certification assessments. Third-party certification is by far the most credible and effective way to drive positive changes through the marketplace.

Certification of management practices — be they in forestry, agriculture, or construction — is not always enough. It is also necessary to track materials as they flow through manufacturing and distribution and are delivered to the market. Without a certified "chain-of-custody" tracking system, there is no real way to ensure that a specific product originates in a certified, well-managed forest, farm, or factory.

EXAMPLES OF 3RD PARTY CERTIFIERS:

Oregon Tilth

Forest Stewardship Council

LEED™

III

LEED CREDITS FOR THE NATURAL CAPITAL CENTER

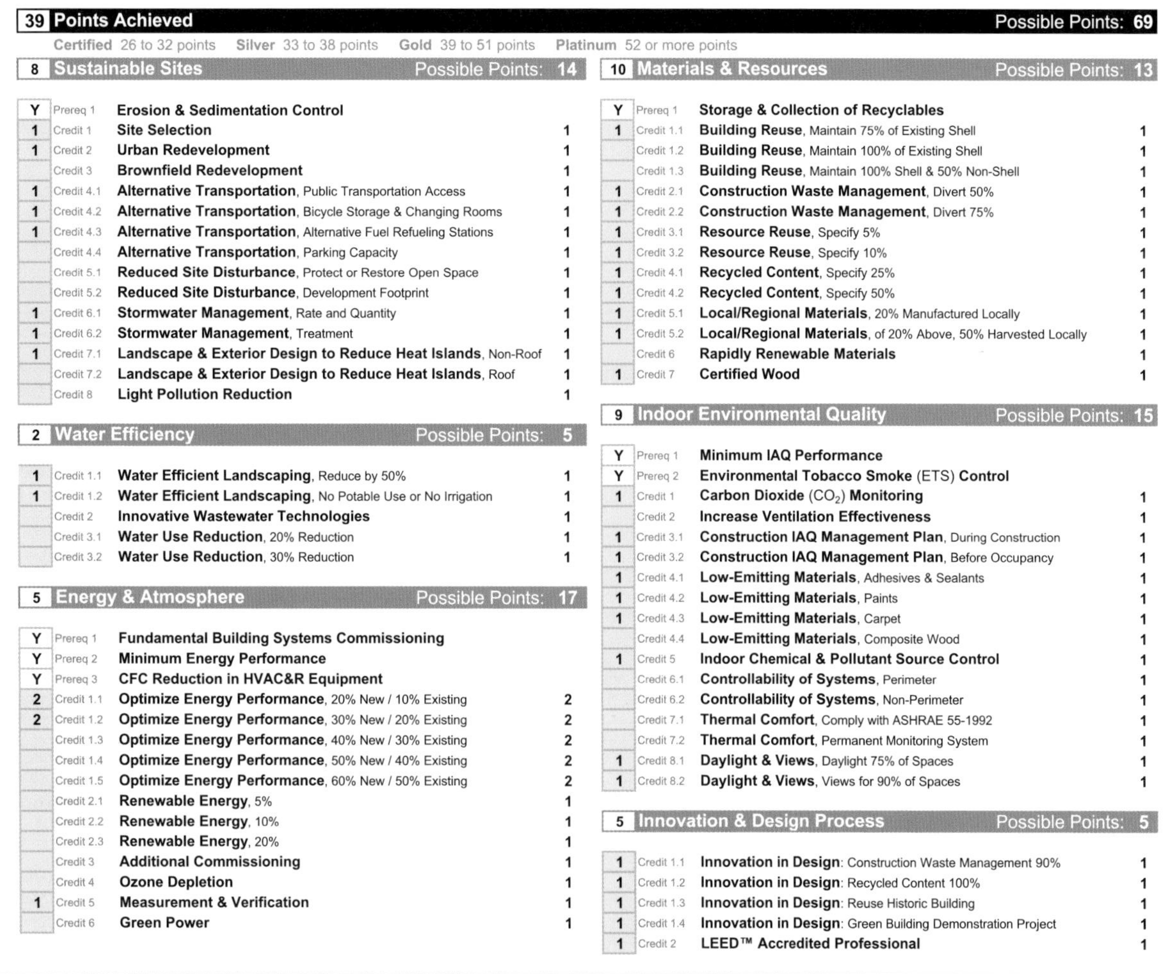

Jean Vollum Natural Capital Center, LEED Project # 0086
LEED Version 2.0 Certification Level: GOLD
December 11, 2001

39 Points Achieved — Possible Points: 69

Certified 26 to 32 points **Silver** 33 to 38 points **Gold** 39 to 51 points **Platinum** 52 or more points

8	Sustainable Sites		Possible Points: 14
Y	Prereq 1	**Erosion & Sedimentation Control**	
1	Credit 1	**Site Selection**	1
1	Credit 2	**Urban Redevelopment**	1
	Credit 3	**Brownfield Redevelopment**	1
1	Credit 4.1	**Alternative Transportation**, Public Transportation Access	1
1	Credit 4.2	**Alternative Transportation**, Bicycle Storage & Changing Rooms	1
1	Credit 4.3	**Alternative Transportation**, Alternative Fuel Refueling Stations	1
	Credit 4.4	**Alternative Transportation**, Parking Capacity	1
	Credit 5.1	**Reduced Site Disturbance**, Protect or Restore Open Space	1
	Credit 5.2	**Reduced Site Disturbance**, Development Footprint	1
1	Credit 6.1	**Stormwater Management**, Rate and Quantity	1
1	Credit 6.2	**Stormwater Management**, Treatment	1
1	Credit 7.1	**Landscape & Exterior Design to Reduce Heat Islands**, Non-Roof	1
	Credit 7.2	**Landscape & Exterior Design to Reduce Heat Islands**, Roof	1
	Credit 8	**Light Pollution Reduction**	1

2	Water Efficiency		Possible Points: 5
1	Credit 1.1	**Water Efficient Landscaping**, Reduce by 50%	1
1	Credit 1.2	**Water Efficient Landscaping**, No Potable Use or No Irrigation	1
	Credit 2	**Innovative Wastewater Technologies**	1
	Credit 3.1	**Water Use Reduction**, 20% Reduction	1
	Credit 3.2	**Water Use Reduction**, 30% Reduction	1

5	Energy & Atmosphere		Possible Points: 17
Y	Prereq 1	**Fundamental Building Systems Commissioning**	
Y	Prereq 2	**Minimum Energy Performance**	
Y	Prereq 3	**CFC Reduction in HVAC&R Equipment**	
2	Credit 1.1	**Optimize Energy Performance**, 20% New / 10% Existing	2
2	Credit 1.2	**Optimize Energy Performance**, 30% New / 20% Existing	2
	Credit 1.3	**Optimize Energy Performance**, 40% New / 30% Existing	2
	Credit 1.4	**Optimize Energy Performance**, 50% New / 40% Existing	2
	Credit 1.5	**Optimize Energy Performance**, 60% New / 50% Existing	2
	Credit 2.1	**Renewable Energy**, 5%	1
	Credit 2.2	**Renewable Energy**, 10%	1
	Credit 2.3	**Renewable Energy**, 20%	1
	Credit 3	**Additional Commissioning**	1
	Credit 4	**Ozone Depletion**	1
1	Credit 5	**Measurement & Verification**	1
	Credit 6	**Green Power**	1

10	Materials & Resources		Possible Points: 13
Y	Prereq 1	**Storage & Collection of Recyclables**	
1	Credit 1.1	**Building Reuse**, Maintain 75% of Existing Shell	1
	Credit 1.2	**Building Reuse**, Maintain 100% of Existing Shell	1
	Credit 1.3	**Building Reuse**, Maintain 100% Shell & 50% Non-Shell	1
1	Credit 2.1	**Construction Waste Management**, Divert 50%	1
1	Credit 2.2	**Construction Waste Management**, Divert 75%	1
1	Credit 3.1	**Resource Reuse**, Specify 5%	1
1	Credit 3.2	**Resource Reuse**, Specify 10%	1
1	Credit 4.1	**Recycled Content**, Specify 25%	1
1	Credit 4.2	**Recycled Content**, Specify 50%	1
1	Credit 5.1	**Local/Regional Materials**, 20% Manufactured Locally	1
1	Credit 5.2	**Local/Regional Materials**, of 20% Above, 50% Harvested Locally	1
	Credit 6	**Rapidly Renewable Materials**	1
1	Credit 7	**Certified Wood**	1

9	Indoor Environmental Quality		Possible Points: 15
Y	Prereq 1	**Minimum IAQ Performance**	
Y	Prereq 2	**Environmental Tobacco Smoke** (ETS) **Control**	
1	Credit 1	**Carbon Dioxide** (CO_2) **Monitoring**	1
	Credit 2	**Increase Ventilation Effectiveness**	1
1	Credit 3.1	**Construction IAQ Management Plan**, During Construction	1
1	Credit 3.2	**Construction IAQ Management Plan**, Before Occupancy	1
1	Credit 4.1	**Low-Emitting Materials**, Adhesives & Sealants	1
1	Credit 4.2	**Low-Emitting Materials**, Paints	1
1	Credit 4.3	**Low-Emitting Materials**, Carpet	1
	Credit 4.4	**Low-Emitting Materials**, Composite Wood	1
1	Credit 5	**Indoor Chemical & Pollutant Source Control**	1
	Credit 6.1	**Controllability of Systems**, Perimeter	1
	Credit 6.2	**Controllability of Systems**, Non-Perimeter	1
	Credit 7.1	**Thermal Comfort**, Comply with ASHRAE 55-1992	1
	Credit 7.2	**Thermal Comfort**, Permanent Monitoring System	1
1	Credit 8.1	**Daylight & Views**, Daylight 75% of Spaces	1
1	Credit 8.2	**Daylight & Views**, Views for 90% of Spaces	1

5	Innovation & Design Process		Possible Points: 5
1	Credit 1.1	**Innovation in Design**: Construction Waste Management 90%	1
1	Credit 1.2	**Innovation in Design**: Recycled Content 100%	1
1	Credit 1.3	**Innovation in Design**: Reuse Historic Building	1
1	Credit 1.4	**Innovation in Design**: Green Building Demonstration Project	1
1	Credit 2	**LEED™ Accredited Professional**	1

Strategies for Integration

Even though the goal of LEED is to foster a holistic approach to creating green buildings, the rating system is divided into six separate categories as a starting place for applicants. They are:

- Sustainable Sites
- Water Efficiency
- Energy & Atmosphere
- Materials & Resources
- Indoor Environmental Quality
- Innovation & Design Process

Starting from one category, a project team can choose to implement integrated strategies that achieve multiple LEED credits. Stormwater management provides an excellent example. Rainwater harvesting assists with on-site stormwater management. Captured and stored rainwater can then provide irrigation for plants on a site, reducing the use of potable water for landscaping. This water can also supply toilets where codes allow, reducing the project's overall water use. With this single measure — rainwater harvesting — a project can earn up to seven points in two categories (Sustainable Sites and Water Efficiency).

The success of integrated strategies depends on early identification and incorporation. If identified early enough, these strategies can be included without significant changes to the budget, schedule, and overall design of the building. In many cases, integrated design solutions reduce overall project costs.

NCC POINTS EARNED		POSSIBLE POINTS
8	SUSTAINABLE SITES	14

This credit category steers development away from inappropriate sites such as agricultural land and natural habitat areas, toward sites that have existing infrastructure and higher density. Credits apply for reducing the impact of development on the site, including the protection and/or restoration of habitat areas, and reducing or treating any stormwater that flows from the site. Sustainable Sites also offers credits for providing environmentally preferable transportation options, mitigating the project's urban heat island effect, and reducing light pollution. (See Cooling Down the Heat Island Effect on page 70.) If a site has not already been selected when the certification process begins, there may be opportunities to locate the project on a site that meets many of the criteria of this credit category.

Bicycle racks in the Natural Capital Center parking lot encourage bicycle use.

The Natural Capital Center earned eight out of a possible 14 points in this category for redeveloping an urban site, providing infrastructure for public and alternative modes of transportation, and managing its stormwater on site.

Notches cut into the curb in the parking lot direct stormwater into the bioswales.

NCC POINTS EARNED		POSSIBLE POINTS
2	WATER EFFICIENCY	5

Water credits encourage project teams to reduce the consumption of potable water for landscape irrigation, sewage conveyance, and other uses in the building. For example, water-efficient landscaping reduces potable water used in irrigation by 50% to 100%, and could earn a project two credits. The Water category also encourages the inclusion of devices that reduce water consumption inside a building. Low-flow plumbing fixtures on faucets or showerheads, waterless urinals, or low-flush toilets, are all strategies that earn credits.

The Natural Capital Center received two points for ensuring that no potable water would be used in landscaping. The Natural Capital Center's site has no permanent irrigation system so that once the plants are established (a period of two to three years) the natural environment will sustain its landscape through the use of native plants.

NCC POINTS EARNED		POSSIBLE POINTS
5	ENERGY & ATMOSPHERE	17

This credit category offers the largest number of points in the rating system, 17 of the total 69 available, for optimizing and commissioning the energy consuming equipment and systems of a building, eliminating the use of ozone depleting refrigerants, and using renewable sources of energy. The first prerequisite for Energy and Atmosphere requires commissioning, a process that verifies that all systems in a building are installed and operating according to the original intent of the design team. Without such verification, a project may not achieve its efficiency goals.

In the Natural Capital Center, the commissioning agent discovered deficiencies and suggested corrections to the mechanical systems in the building, such as changing the factory settings for the air conditioning/heating system, resulting in energy savings valued at $5,400 annually. These savings alone will pay for the cost of the commissioning process within five years of the building's operation.

The HVAC system is an efficient, variable air-volume design.

LEED supports ozone protection protocols by encouraging a phase-out of **CFCs** in air-conditioning and refrigeration equipment and provides a point for the use of non-HCFC refrigerants, such as **HFCs**. While the air conditioning system in the Natural Capital Center uses an **HCFC** refrigerant, the refrigerant that was selected has a significantly reduced ozone depletion potential compared to CFCs and is more energy efficient than many HFC refrigerants. This was enough to meet the prerequisite for CFC reduction, but not to earn it a credit for reducing global warming impact.

CFCs, **HFCs**, and **HCFCs** are all chemicals in the fluorocarbon family. Organic compounds made of fluorine, chlorine, and other elements, they have properties that make them very useful in refrigerants, air conditioners, and insulation. CFCs (chlorofluorocarbons) were used most widely, until scientists discovered that when they got high in the atmosphere they were breaking down the planet's ozone layer. The ozone layer is critical to life on earth as it filters out harmful ultraviolet (UV) radiation. HCFCs (halogenated fluorocarbons) are not as ozone-depleting as CFCs, so they were introduced as a temporary replacement for CFCs. HFCs (hydrofluorocarbons) are presently the best alternative to CFCs since they do not cause any ozone depletion. Scientists are still working on a better overall solution to the problem of chemical refrigerants, since even HFCs are considered a greenhouse gas and contribute to another serious environmental problem in the earth's atmosphere — global warming.

Among the Energy and Atmosphere credits, optimizing energy performance is critical, as a project can earn up to ten points. This is the single largest category of points in the LEED rating system, reflecting the importance of overall energy use to a building's ecological footprint. Two approaches are typical in building design: the linear, non-integrated process, where more efficient systems are added incrementally; or the integrated process, which requires a strong collaboration among the architect, engineer, and energy modeler. When systems such as air conditioning, heating, and lighting are added one at a time they can end up oversized, adding significant costs to a project. In the second scenario, the team examines every way possible to decrease energy use, cut unwanted solar heat gain, and reduce artificial lighting, resulting in a far more integrated, and often more effective, energy system.

The engineering team for the Natural Capital Center employed a computer program that provides a whole building energy use simulation to predict the heating and cooling requirements for the building. Whole building energy simulations use a computer model that includes the geometry, heating and lighting equipment, energy loads and envelope (exterior shell) of a building. The design team had to add or subtract various energy efficiency measures in the computer model to determine which strategies made the most sense for the building. The model analyzes the "first cost" and "payback in years" of various alternative measures so that the design team can select the best option.

A measurement and verification credit, also within the Energy and Atmosphere category, applies to projects in which meters and monitors are installed to track the energy use of primary components. The Natural Capital Center was designed for this type of monitoring, which will allow the building operators to see if they are obtaining the actual efficiencies projected by the energy use simulation performed during design. Using an integrated approach, the Natural Capital Center's design team was able to reduce the size of the mechanical system and realize a 21% improvement in energy savings beyond the Oregon Energy Code. This is significant given that this historic building maintains much of its original character. The Natural Capital Center was awarded five out of a possible 17 points for Energy and Atmosphere.

NCC POINTS EARNED		POSSIBLE POINTS
10	MATERIALS & RESOURCES	13

The LEED rating system provides numerous opportunities for projects to reduce their overall environmental impact simply based on the materials used in the building. The Materials and Resources category considers building reuse, construction waste salvaging and recycling, the use of locally harvested and manufactured materials, certified wood and rapidly renewable materials (materials that regenerate within ten years).

The Natural Capital Center received a point for building reuse by maintaining 75% of the existing shell of the 1895 warehouse. LEED offers additional points for using an even greater percentage of building shell and non-shell elements where possible.

Large steel doors from the original warehouse were salvaged, cleaned, and re-installed in the Ecotrust Conference Center.

Two credits are also available for recycling and/or salvaging at least 50% to 75% of construction waste. The general contractor for the Natural Capital Center, Walsh Construction, exceeded both of these benchmarks by diverting 98% of the construction waste from landfills, thereby earning the project two points for construction waste management. The project earned an additional point in the Innovation & Design category for its exceptional recycling rate. The Natural Capital Center earned ten out of a possible 13 points in the Materials and Resources category.

One of the more significant efforts to reduce the environmental impact of the Natural Capital Center is immediately apparent as you enter the building. The rich character of exposed brick, salvaged timbers and industrial building parts is evident througout the building. Wherever possible, the owner, design team and the contractor worked to incorporate reused materials into new construction in the building — elements salvaged from the original structure or from nearby buildings that were being demolished. Some materials such as brick and doors were used in their original form, while much of the wood was resawn on-site to be used as structural members, doors, windows, paneling and trim. This effort substantially reduced the need for new materials while also reducing the amount of demolition and construction waste generated by the project. Two points were earned in the Resources Reuse credit for the salvage and reuse of materials in the building. Where new wood was required, FSC certified wood was used, earning another LEED point. Preference was also given for materials that were manufactured and/or harvested regionally (defined by LEED as within 500 miles) in order to reduce the environmental impact of transportation and to support producers, manufacturers, and suppliers. The project earned two points for using regionally produced materials.

Operable windows are located throughout the second and third floors.

NCC POINTS EARNED		POSSIBLE POINTS
9	INDOOR ENVIRONMENTAL QUALITY	15

The indoor environmental quality of a building has a significant impact on the health and productivity of its occupants. LEED encourages improvements to the indoor environment by providing prerequisites and credits for eliminating indoor pollution sources from the building, improving ventilation and thermal comfort, and providing building occupants with natural daylight and a connection to the outdoors.

Ecotrust received nine out of 15 possible points for using paints and carpeting with low levels of toxicity, for installing carbon dioxide monitors in the HVAC system, and for protecting the mechanical system from collecting dust and debris during construction. The building also provides daylight in 75% of the regularly occupied spaces and views to the outdoors from 90% of the regularly occupied spaces, both important factors for employee satisfaction and productivity. Low-emitting materials in the form of adhesives, sealants, paints, and carpet also earned points.

NCC POINTS EARNED		POSSIBLE POINTS
5	INNOVATION AND DESIGN PROCESS	5

Innovation credits are awarded to a project for either substantially exceeding the requirements of an existing credit or by achieving a measurable environmental improvement that is not included in the credits of the current rating system. All green building projects have the potential for significant innovation. This may be related to the mission or goals of the building occupant or owner, the type of building, or the activities that take place inside the building.

Ecotrust obtained all five of the possible innovation points through the following strategies:

- The Natural Capital Center is open daily as a green building demonstration project to the public and interested parties, with ample interpretive material throughout the building and regular weekly tours.
- The project protects and preserves a local historic building through redevelopment as a mixed-use green building.
- Two innovation credits recognized the significant performance in construction waste management and the use of building materials with high recycled content.
- A final point was awarded for involving a LEED accredited professional through all phases of the design and construction.

The LEED plaque at the western entrance is one stop on the Natural Capital Center's interpretive trail that guides visitors through the building.

LEED AND PUBLIC AGENCIES

Local and state governments are the most frequent users of the LEED™ rating system. The City of Portland passed an ordinance requiring LEED certification for all new city buildings, the City of Seattle established a policy for municipal buildings to meet the LEED Silver rating, and the states of Maryland and Pennsylvania have recently passed building requirements tied to LEED. Many other state and local governments have adopted a requirement that government funded projects achieve LEED Certification, or provide incentives for LEED projects. With government mandating the building community to meet these guidelines for public projects, the industry is forced to adapt, further transforming the marketplace. In 2002 LEED achieved over a 22% market penetration in the public sector, meaning that 22% of new construction square footage by federal, state, and local governments was registered with LEED.

Along with interest in incorporating LEED measurements in their own buildings, many governments have created incentives that encourage LEED in commercial and institutional buildings. The City of Portland's green building initiative is tied to LEED and leverages local expertise to develop cost-effective solutions for builders, developers, and building owners and users. The Oregon Office of Energy recently added a tax incentive for LEED certification, through which projects can now receive a tax credit for green building projects achieving a LEED Silver or higher. The amount of the credit increases with each rise in the level of certification. ■

The Portland Communications Center, which houses the city's 911 dispatch, was designed and constructed in accordance with the City of Portland's new green building initiative.

incremental energy efficiency measures often add to the construction cost of a project, but provide a return on the initial investment by reducing operating costs. This relationship between incremental efficiency and cost will hold true for most projects up to an energy use reduction of about 40% relative to the state energy code. If an integrated design process begins early in a project, however, a design team may be able to achieve energy savings far greater than 40% with *minimal* construction cost increase or perhaps even a *cost savings*.

Documentation is a crucial part of the LEED process. It must show that applicants understand the intent and meet the requirements of each prerequisite or credit. Although documentation varies for each prerequisite or credit, it is collected throughout the design and construction phases, and submitted to the USGBC at the conclusion of the project. The recent release of the new LEED 2.1 version of the Rating System includes a spreadsheet, or Letter Template, for each credit. Using the template, the project team can declare the fulfillment of the requirements of each credit and may only be asked to provide the documentation if a specific credit is audited. With this new process the USGBC expects to audit roughly 30% of the credits, further streamlining the overall documentation and certification process.

Conclusion

LEED is transforming the marketplace from the inside out. The volunteer professionals who created LEED purposely selected recognized industry standards to help guide the building industry toward more sustainable practices. After examining green building measures used by organizations and states across the nation, they chose the top standards to apply to LEED. The credibility of these models greatly facilitated the adoption of LEED by the building industry. Today, when architects and engineers write specifications to address LEED goals, contractors must push their suppliers to find and manufacture products that meet these objectives — creating new demand in the market and encouraging the marketplace to respond.

In July of 2003, with over 943 projects (128 million square feet) registered nationwide, LEED captured 3% of all commercial project construction by square footage. This is an impressive figure for a three-year-old program. Sixty projects representing approximately nine million square feet have been certified to date. The program has also been enthusiastically embraced by public agencies across the country (see **LEED and Public Agencies** at left), which will increase these figures over time.

LEED continues to expand its reach within the building industry. The USGBC is integrating LEED into other segments of the building market, designing new LEED "products" or rating systems specifically for those areas. Programs now under development include LEED for Existing Buildings, LEED for Commercial Interiors, LEED Core & Shell, LEED for Multiple Buildings, and LEED Homes.

Since the Natural Capital Center received its Gold Certification in 2001, many new green projects in Portland and throughout the United States have emerged. These numbers illustrate the growing attraction of green building and the role of LEED in defining and stimulating the market. ■

RAPID TRANSFER & STORAGE CO.
SOUTHERN PACIFIC
THE MILWAUKEE ROAD

WORKING WITH HISTORY

by Bob Naito

It is no coincidence that Jane Jacobs' *The Death and Life of Great American Cities* (1961) and Rachel Carson's *Silent Spring* (1962) were published within a year of each other. These landmark books, each in its own way, changed the course of history. In a decade that became anything but silent, *Silent Spring* planted the seeds of the environmental movement. The *Death and Life of Great American Cities* forever changed the way we think about our metropolises. Since the 1960s, the historic preservation and the environmental movements have grown up together and been closely aligned. The primary difference between them is that historic preservationists are concerned with protection of the built environment and environmentalists with the natural environment.

Honoring the Legacy of Old Buildings

It is easy to forget how new American cities and buildings are when compared with those of the rest of the world. Consider one of the most famous buildings, St. Paul's Cathedral in London. The architectural significance and historical importance of St. Paul's make it one of the world's preeminent historic landmarks. The first St. Paul's Cathedral was built almost 1400 years ago in 604. Rebuilt after a fire and again after being ransacked by Vikings, it took two centuries to complete Old St. Paul's in 1310 — almost two centuries before Europeans reached the New World. After it was destroyed in the Great Fire of London, Sir Christopher Wren was commissioned to produce a new design that was completed in 1697 — over a century before the Lewis and Clark expedition would reach the Pacific Ocean and nearly 200 years before the Natural Capital Center was first built in 1895.

In contrast, the relatively short history of American cities and their architecture is one of unprecedented change brought about by economic expansion and technological advances. As these young American cities grew and new technology allowed the construction of taller and taller buildings, individual structures, entire blocks, and even whole neighborhoods were demolished in the name of progress. The modern skyscraper, mass-production of the automobile, the interstate freeway system, urban renewal, suburbia, and the shopping mall are quintessential American inventions that transformed American cities, often for the worse.

Follow the → → → → to the Largest Freight Terminal in Northwest -:- Dependable Lines to All Points

PORTLAND TRUCK TERMINAL INC.
Phone BR. 9461

MODERN CONVENIENT WEST SIDE FREIGHT CENTER

In a previous life, the Natural Capital Center served as a freight center for trucking and rail distribution.

The building's lobby and atrium are open and inviting to encourage chance meetings and conversations, while showcasing historical features such as the original posts and beams.

In *The Death and Life of Great American Cities*, Jane Jacobs described the failures of post-war planning in American cities:

> "But look what we have built ... low-income projects that become worse centers of delinquency, vandalism and general social hopelessness than the slums they were supposed to replace.... Cultural centers that are unable to support a good bookstore. Civic centers that are avoided by everyone but bums.... Promenades that go from no place to nowhere and have no promenaders. Expressways that eviscerate great cities. This is not the rebuilding of cities. This is the sacking of cities."[1]

In the 1960s, Jacobs' book became a call to arms for preservationists, architects, planners, and ordinary citizens defending their neighborhoods and the old buildings within them. In a 1979 article for *Historic Preservation* titled "Preservationists are Un-American," Clem Labine made a connection between historic preservation and conservation long before the concept of sustainable development was recognized.

> "America was built on the concept of the frontier. Land was limitless. Resources were never ending. The pioneer way was to use it up, throw it away and move on... Preservationists oppose the conventional idea of consuming even more. We are actually the new wave of pioneer. We are struggling to reverse the 'use it up and move on' mentality. We are moving in and picking up the pieces. We are taking individual buildings and whole neighborhoods that have been discarded and trying to make them live again."[2]

Before the 1960s, historic preservation initiatives in the United States were primarily local efforts and were limited to the restoration of established landmarks of national significance. The National Trust for Historic Preservation was founded in 1949 based on a similar institution in Britain. In the 1960s, the Trust and other preservation organizations lobbied for a national policy on historic preservation. In 1966, the United States Congress passed the National Historic Preservation Act. The Act is the most important historic preservation legislation ever approved. It created the National Register of Historic Places administered by the National Park Service, established a national advisory council on historic preservation, and designated State Historic Preservation Officers in all fifty states. Historic preservation became a major public policy goal in its own right. Since the Act, over 72,000 properties have been listed on the National Register. Local landmark commissions and preservation organizations now have their counterparts on the state and national levels. Today there are 3,000 preservation organizations in the United States and the membership in the National Trust for Historic Preservation has grown from 10,700 in 1966 to over 250,000 in 2003.

The Case for Historic Rehabilitation

As a society we have come to recognize that historic buildings have value beyond their historical and architectural significance. Where historic preservation had been defined as the strict restoration of historic buildings to their original condition and use, the term has gradually broadened to include rehabilitation and adaptive use of historic buildings — giving them a second life in a new use. The conversion of the McCraken warehouse to the Natural Capital Center is one example.

Some older buildings are valuable for what they contribute to their neighborhood. As one author put it, they are "a gift to the street" whose architectural style, character, and charm (and maybe even eccentricity) enrich and enliven their surroundings. These buildings are worth saving because our communities would be less interesting, less attractive, without them. In *The Death and Life of Great American Cities* Jane Jacobs wrote:

> "Cities need old buildings so badly it is probably impossible for vigorous streets and districts to grow without them... For really new ideas of any kind — no matter how ultimately profitable or otherwise successful some of them might prove to be — there is no leeway for such chancy trial, error and experimentation in the high-overhead economy of new construction. Old ideas can sometimes use new buildings. New ideas must use old buildings."[3]

That experimenting with new ideas should take place in old buildings instead of new construction may seem counterintuitive, but it does make sense. The Natural Capital Center is a case in point. Ecotrust was able to experiment with green building strategies because it was working with an existing site — one that provided a palette of brick and timber that could easily accommodate new design ideas. The pre-existing framework was a perfect counterpart for new green elements such as bioswales, an ecoroof, or extensive daylighting with windows and skylights. The large open spaces of the warehouse coincided with Ecotrust's vision for community and collaboration, allowing room in the overall design for places to meet, create, and connect informally. Finally, the very nature of the warehouse itself, a relic of the economic and social history of the Pacific Northwest, embodied many of Ecotrust's goals for developing a regional identity known as Salmon Nation. The cost and risk of the Natural Capital Center redevelopment would have been much greater if Ecotrust had attempted to apply the same vision to a brand new building. It would be difficult even to know where to begin.

The Rapid Transfer Company purchased the McCraken warehouse in 1941, warehousing and distributing goods in the Pacific Northwest.

HISTORY OF THE McCRAKEN WAREHOUSE

Simply as a survivor, the McCraken warehouse would have had intrinsic historical value, but the building has a history of its own and is architecturally significant as well. Built by John McCraken around 1895, the warehouse's flat roof and parapet, recessed round-arched entry, arched window openings, stucco and brick facing, and massive heavy appearance make it a classic example of the Richardsonian Romanesque style. This style flourished between 1885 and 1900, and was chosen for many of Portland's commercial buildings during this time, including Union Station, just two blocks east of the warehouse.

In the late 1800s Portland stood poised for growth. The recently completed transcontinental railroad, improved shipping capabilities at the port, and several key real estate and business investments, assured Portland's future as a center for transportation and distribution. The city's population was steadily growing — between 1890 and 1900 it increased by 50%. The city was recovering from a recession and seeing increased construction and retail activity, along with the establishment of new residential neighborhoods. Businesses realized the opportunities for expansion and many built and moved into new buildings in the commercial and industrial centers. McCraken, a wholesale building supplies distributor, erected the building to accommodate his growing business.

In a period of extensive rail transportation in northwest Portland, the warehouse was ideally located between two freight yards — the Southern Pacific-Northern Pacific, and the Spokane-Portland-Seattle. A short distance away was the Union Pacific's freight yard. Short rail spurs, known as team tracks, ran alongside the building's loading docks, with enough space in between them for teams of horses or trucks. Teams of horses, known as dray teams, could also move through the center of the building, using concrete ramps. McCraken's Irving Street warehouse had a long history of use by storage and distributing companies. In the early 1930s the building was known as the Central Truck Terminal, and at times as many as thirty trucking companies are listed as occupying the address. A small company could rent a door or two and operate its truck line from that location. Until 1940, a café was located inside near the front office, available to all who worked in the building. The last owner, Rapid Transfer & Storage, occupied the warehouse until 1997, while the rest of the block was leased as a commercial parking lot. Ecotrust purchased the site in 1998. ■

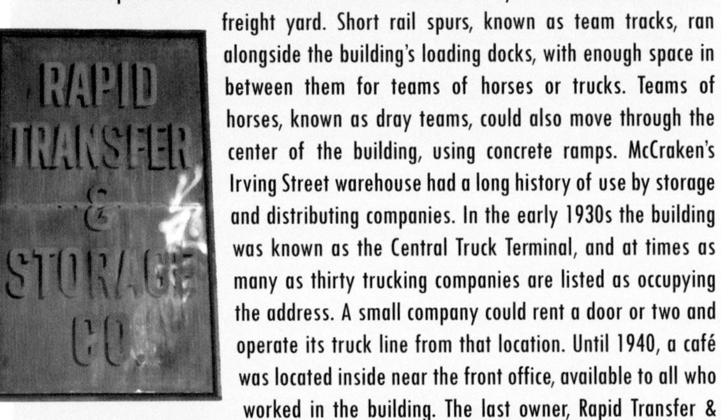

The Forces Against Preservation — The McCraken Warehouse As a Case in Point

Portland was no exception to the urban problems described in *The Death and Life of Great American Cities*. In the 1950s, urban renewal was used to demolish an entire neighborhood in South Portland to make way for a new civic center. New interstate freeways cut existing neighborhoods in two. Lloyd Center, one of the first regional shopping malls in the United States, stole what vitality was left in the downtown retail district. Portland, which was the repository of the largest collection of 1890s cast-iron architecture west of Chicago, watched as one after another historic building was demolished to make way, not even for a new building, but for a parking lot.

In the late 1960s, progressive civic leaders responded to these problems with an innovative Downtown Plan, which laid the groundwork for the public and private development that would successfully transform the downtown over the next thirty years. Portland's zoning code was amended to put a limit on the total number of parking spaces in downtown and to prohibit new surface parking lots. New pedestrian friendly buildings were required to be built to the sidewalk with entrances and windows facing the street. The City created a downtown transit mall to provide better bus circulation and added light-rail trains and streetcars to the public transit system. At the state level, Oregon's pioneering land-use laws created urban growth boundaries to contain sprawl and encourage "smart" growth.

The Downtown Plan also recognized the importance of historic preservation to the character and vitality of the city. New historic districts were established and new state tax incentives (together with the federal tax credit, see discussion below) were created to encourage the preservation of historic buildings. Ironically, the very success of Portland in revitalizing its downtown ultimately threatened the city's remaining inventory of historic buildings.

By 1998 when Ecotrust acquired the McCraken warehouse, there were very few surviving buildings from the first fifty years of Portland's history. For example, out of 163 downtown office buildings, only five were built before 1900, and almost half of the buildings dated from 1950 or later.

The McCraken warehouse was in this precarious position because of all of the new development taking place in the River District. The national economy was booming, the dot.com bubble was still expanding, and the real estate market in the River District was very hot. Construction tower cranes were sprouting up for new condominium and apartment projects on every side of the building. Even as the rehabilitation of the McCraken warehouse was underway, its neighbor to the south, another turn-of-the-century warehouse, was demolished to make way for an apartment building.

Encouraging Historic Renovation

Prior to 1976, the U.S. tax code favored the demolition of older buildings over saving and using them. With the passage of the Tax Reform Act of 1976, the tax code became aligned with national historic preservation policy to encourage voluntary, private sector investment in conserving historic buildings. The Act created a historic rehabilitation tax credit equal to 25% of the cost of restoring a historic building (reduced to 20% in 1986). Many states followed suit and enacted their own tax credits or property tax abatements to make rehabilitation more affordable.

These federal and state historic preservation tax incentives have proven an invaluable tool for revitalizing communities and preserving historic buildings, and in many cities, entire historic districts. Tax incentive programs generate jobs during construction and after the buildings are put back in service. Rehabilitation of historic buildings attracts new private investment to the historic districts of cities and towns and is crucial to the long-term economic health of many communities. Since 1976, the historic preservation tax incentives in the U.S. have produced the following benefits:

- More than 27,000 historic properties rehabilitated and saved
- Over $22 billion in private rehabilitation stimulated
- More than 149,000 housing units rehabilitated and 75,000 housing units created, over 30,000 of which are low and moderate-income units.[4]

Moving inventory at the McCraken warehouse in the late 1940s or early 1950s.

For a restoration project like the Natural Capital Center, developers often use the historic rehabilitation tax credit to provide a source of additional equity. The amount of the historic rehabilitation tax credit is 20% of eligible costs. Non-historic rehabilitations of buildings over fifty years old may qualify for a 10% credit. The Internal Revenue Service (IRS) and the National Park Service dually administer the credit. The IRS determines various tax rules, such as what costs generate credits. The Park Service reviews compliance with the architectural standards and issues certificates of conformance for the historic tax credit. In order to qualify for the historic tax credit the National Park Service requires that the rehabilitation meet the Secretary of the Interior's Standards for Rehabilitation (see The Secretary's Standards for HIstoric Rehabilitation on page 44).

THE SECRETARY'S STANDARDS FOR HISTORIC REHABILITATION[5]

1. The property shall be used for its historic purpose or placed in a new use that requires minimal change to the defining characteristics of the building.

2. The historic character of the building shall be preserved.

3. Each property shall be recognized as a physical record of its time, place, and use.

4. Changes to the building that have taken place over time and have taken on historic significance shall be preserved.

5. Distinctive features, finishes, and construction techniques or examples of craftsmanship shall be preserved.

6. Deteriorated historic features shall be repaired rather than replaced. Where they are beyond repair, the replacements shall match the old in design, color, texture, and other visual qualities and, where possible, materials.

7. Chemical or physical treatments, such as sandblasting, that cause damage to historic materials shall not be used.

8. Significant archeological resources affected by a project shall be protected and preserved.

9. New additions, exterior alterations, or related new construction shall not destroy historic materials that characterize the building. The new work shall be differentiated from the old and shall be compatible with the massing, size, scale, and architectural features to protect the historic integrity of the property and its environment.

10. New additions and adjacent or related new construction shall be undertaken in such a manner that if removed in the future, the essential form and integrity of the historic property and its environment would be unimpaired. ■

After the rehabilitation is completed, the entire credit amount is available to reduce taxes. However, property owners sometimes find that they cannot use the entire credit because of the amount of their tax liability or restrictions imposed by other areas of the tax law, such as passive activities, alternative minimum tax, and at-risk rules. Accordingly, some property owners opt to sell the credits to a third party not subject to these limitations. The proceeds of the tax credit sale provide additional project equity reducing the amount of the mortgage or the developer's equity requirement. The credits accrue only to property owners, so these transactions are structured as partnerships or limited liability companies with credit purchasers. Historic tax credit investors are typically Fortune 500 corporations, banks, or tax credit syndicators. In the case of the Natural Capital Center, a syndicator assisted Ecotrust in identifying an investor with an appetite for tax credits.

Historic Preservation and Green Building

As with green building, renovating a historic structure rather than building anew has triple bottom line benefits:

Economic Returns

While historic preservation does have costs, not preserving may well cost even more. Demolition — tearing down a building and trucking the construction debris to a landfill — is costly. More significantly, while renovating a historic building may or may not be more expensive than new construction in hard costs to the individual owner, it provides society with substantial savings. Expensive public infrastructure like roads, sidewalks, transit, water and sewer systems, and gas and electric utilities are already in place, whereas they must be created and maintained when building on open space. On top of these savings, historic restoration also increases property values in the area.

Environmental Returns

Historic renovation is recycling on a grand scale. Each time an old building is converted to a new use it saves a tremendous amount of wood, steel, concrete, glass, and other materials that would otherwise go into a new building. These savings are in addition to all of the public infrastructure costs cited above.

Social Returns

Just as green buildings reinforce people's connection to natural systems, historic buildings reinforce a community's connection to its past. When adapted for a new use, these buildings provide a vital cultural link between a society's past, its present, and its future. In many cases, historic renovation also encourages private investment in depressed neighborhoods, giving communities new hope for the future.

Despite Ecotrust's initial misgivings, it was delighted to discover that the historic standards were consistent with both green building and its architectural vision for the Natural Capital Center. The desire to create interior spaces with minimal enclosures and to preserve the high ceilings and exposed heavy timber construction fit the historic standards because this preserved the character of the old warehouse. This approach also meant using fewer new materials in the project, meeting one of Ecotrust's goals for sustainability.

There were some conflicts between historic preservation and green building goals. For example, the energy efficiency of the building could have been improved by replacing the historic wood windows with new energy efficient ones and covering the interior side of the exterior brick walls with insulation and sheetrock. Instead Ecotrust chose to repair the historic windows, a requirement of the historic standards and part of Ecotrust's design. Covering the exterior walls with sheetrock was not acceptable because it would have changed the very character of the building that attracted Ecotrust in the first place. Nor would it have met the historic standards. In order to meet both the LEED requirements for energy efficiency and the historic standards, the electrical engineer used computer energy modeling to select a more energy efficient HVAC system.

Conclusion

Minor conflicts-of-interest aside, the over-arching similarities between historic preservation and green building are striking. The synergy between the two movements can be irresistible, providing unique opportunities for design and innovation. The conversion of the McCraken warehouse into the Natural Capital Center is only one example. Others will continue to emerge as historic neighborhoods are revitalized and green building gains momentum — it is only a matter of time. ■

THE ENDURING SONG
TBA

by Bettina von Hagen and Bob Naito

Ecotrust purchased the McCraken warehouse in 1998 for redevelopment into the Natural Capital Center. The building had stood the test of time: over 100 years old, it was structurally sound, well situated, open and inviting, with a beautiful palette of wood and brick. While these qualities attracted us to the building, they also intimidated us. Could we renovate the building successfully, bringing it up to current codes and new uses without impairing its fundamental qualities? A century from now, would our additions and occupancy live up to the high standards established in the first hundred years of the building's life, both in terms of aesthetics and of relevance to the surrounding neighborhood and city?

With these thoughts in mind, we spent two years developing the program, selecting the building team, performing financial analyses, and raising capital before starting the redevelopment in earnest in the spring of 2000. As first-time developers we had a lot to learn, and many goals and ambitions to reconcile with harsh financial constraints. We were enticed not only by green building and a careful restoration of our historic structure, but also by our desire to construct a physical representation of our mission. As described in the Introduction, we hoped to create a marketplace for the goods, services, and products of the emerging conservation economy, an ambitious goal with significant implications for design, construction, tenant selection, and operations. We also had to distill our ambitions into a concise and compelling program and financial projections that would appeal to both our philanthropic donors and our conventional lenders, and comply with zoning and building, structural, and seismic codes that were in flux. Finally, we had to anticipate and respond to the rapidly changing nature of the neighborhood.

Setting Our Sights

Our first step was to clarify and describe our objectives:

- **Create a center for the conservation economy:** We wanted to create a tangible marketplace where even the casual visitor would become intrigued by the conservation economy — through the products, services, and information

The Natural Capital Center in 1998, shortly after Ecotrust's purchase.

RIVER DISTRICT REDEVELOPMENT

Selected by *Money Magazine* in 2000 as the country's most livable city, Portland, Oregon serves as a national model for successful management of urban growth issues. The Natural Capital Center is located in Portland's River District, a vibrant new neighborhood being created in an old industrial area of existing warehouse buildings and 34 acres of what were vacant rail yards.

The history of the River District began in 1991 when an ad hoc group of business leaders spent six months developing a vision for the area north of downtown. Their vision called for a high-density urban residential neighborhood to house a resident population of 15,000 and provide jobs, services, and recreation for Portland's central city. The City of Portland has committed to financing 2,000 units of affordable housing. Historic warehouses have been converted into residential lofts above new art galleries, retail shops, and trendy restaurants. New residential buildings have been constructed to provide both subsidized and market rate rentals and condominiums.[1]

The fountain at Jamison Square Park, with the Natural Capital Center in the background.

The most visible public investment in the neighborhood is Portland Streetcar, which stops in front of the Natural Capital Center. Located kitty-corner from the Natural Capital Center, Jamison Square opened in 2002, the first of three new parks planned for the River District. In the summer, its water feature attracts children and their parents from around the city. A thriving artists' community also energizes the neighborhood and the first Thursday of each month brings hundreds of visitors to local art galleries. Despite the handful of cranes and pile drivers that still dot the horizon of northwest Portland, the River District is already well on its way to becoming a new, vital center for Portland life, work, and play. ■

available, as well as the general feel of the building. It was therefore very important to assemble the right group of tenants, representing industries that shape the landscape in Salmon Nation: fisheries, food and farming, forestry, investing, and green building. Our goal was also to stimulate formal and informal gatherings for the general public, and in the design process we ended up with four primary public spaces: a 2,200 square foot conference center for formal meetings; a generous, light-filled atrium with tables, chairs, and information screens for informal encounters; a 3,000 square foot rooftop terrace, and an "interpretive trail" which winds around the building and tells the story of the Natural Capital Center, its tenants, and the conservation economy.

- **Invite collaboration and community among tenants:** Given our desire to spur the creation of a restorative economy, we recognized the need for impromptu encounters and formal collaboration among building tenants, all of whom are leaders in some sector of this new economy (see **The Community of Tenants** on page 108). We held a design charette with prospective tenants, led by *Workplace by Design* authors Franklin Becker and Fritz Steele. The charette focused on interior design and the creation of workspaces that would invite interaction and partnerships. Our design objectives included shared space, such as conference rooms, seating areas, and kitchens, and flexible workplace build-out to encourage innovation and collaboration (see Chapter 9 for more detail).

- **Retain the building's historic character:** Although the decision to place the building on the National Register of Historic Places and seek historic rehabilitation tax credits came later, we knew we wanted to restore the building's façade and maintain its graceful arched doorways and windows. The building, which occupied half of the block, was divided down the center by a load-bearing brick wall. Other than that it was quite open, with a 200-foot-long north to south span, high ceilings supported by beautiful old-growth Douglas-fir posts and beams, and original Douglas-fir plank floors. Our goal was to maintain the openness and views, to minimize the use of floor-to-ceiling walls, and to retain as much of the original brick and timbers as possible.

- **Incorporate green building:** We wanted the building restoration to incorporate practical and appropriate green building strategies, minimizing the use of materials and energy and maximizing the distribution of natural light and fresh air. We paid particular attention to reusing materials and managing stormwater on site. (The following three chapters describe these strategies in detail.)

- **Build a permanent headquarters for Ecotrust:** Approaching our ten-year anniversary, we knew we needed a permanent home that reflected our values and objectives. We also wanted to stop paying rent, start building equity, and earn money to support our core programs.

The Nuts, Bolts, and Bricks of the Renovation

The Development Plan

With our ambitions outlined, we knew we needed an experienced developer to turn our objectives into a fundable and profitable building program and development plan. We turned to Bob Naito, an experienced and creative developer who has been involved in many historic rehabilitation projects in Portland. In addition to instinctively understanding the complexity and magic of combining historic and green redevelopment objectives, Bob had another advantage; his partner, John Tess, was one of the nation's leading consultants on historic rehabilitation.

Bob began by helping us explore alternative development strategies for the property—from a low-cost, minimalist scheme to one that realized the maximum development potential of the block. The existing zoning permitted office, retail and residential uses in a 75-foot tall building. If more than 10,000 square feet of new construction were added to the site, the code required the construction of a minimum of 14 housing units. The zoning also limited building to a 4:1 FAR (floor-to-area ratio), meaning that our 40,000 square foot block was limited to a 160,000 square foot structure.

Although the full development strategy (a 160,000 square foot build-out) yielded the highest net present value, it would have required substantially more equity, complicated our program by adding a housing component, and presented significantly more risk. Instead, we chose an intermediate strategy that saved the historic warehouse building and added a 10,000 square foot penthouse to the roof. We decided to use the remaining half block for parking and stormwater management. Given Ecotrust's limited development experience, we felt the budget and program were more manageable, and we liked the idea of

HIGHLIGHTS OF THE RESTORATION

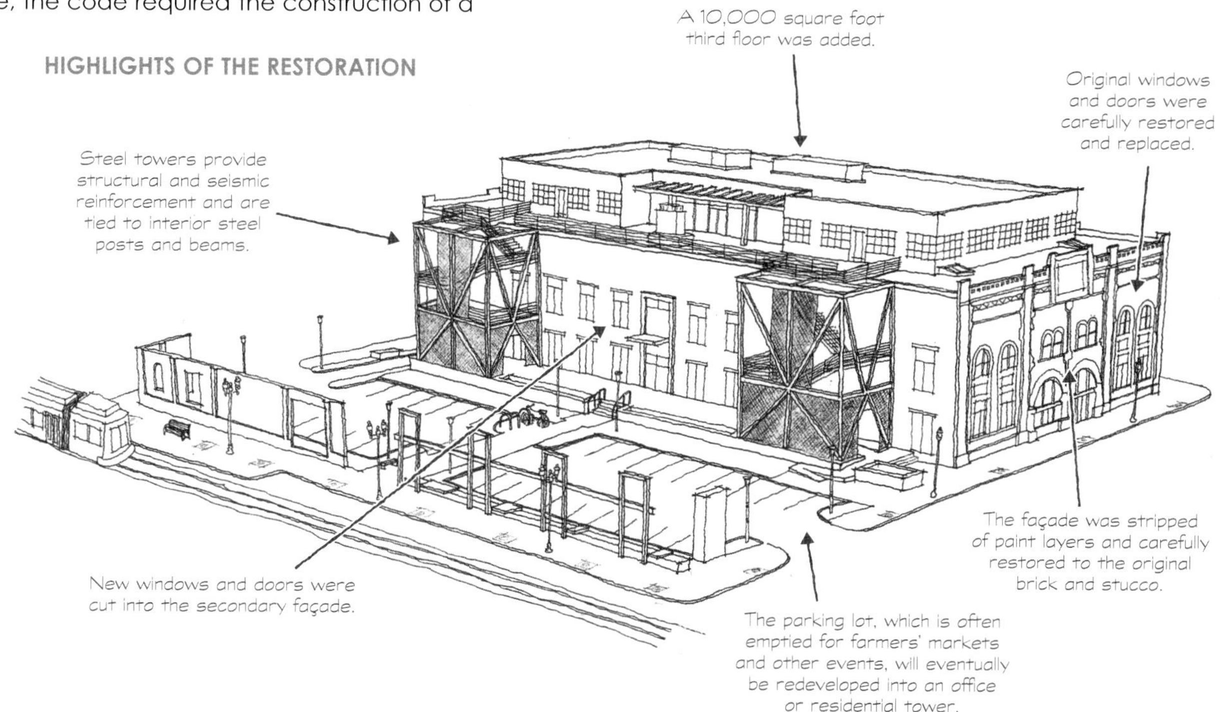

V

TENANT IMPROVEMENT GUIDELINES

Each new tenant was given a set of Tenant Improvement Guidelines which described the Natural Capital Center's design principles, environmental goals, and requirements for construction waste management. The guidelines also recommended materials and products and appropriate installation methods for brick masonry, metals, wood and plastics, insulation, sealants, doors, finishes, carpets, interior paint and wood treatments, HVAC and plumbing, and electrical components.

Ecotrust also invited tenants to participate in design charettes with *Workplace by Design* authors Franklin Becker and Fritz Steele. Charette participants discussed the building's design principles in detail and brainstormed strategies to achieve natural light and fresh air, a nontoxic work environment, flexible office design, and connections among tenants.

Masons from Walsh Construction carefully constructed a new arch, copying the original arch to the right, to provide better circulation in the Patagonia store.

Some tenants chose to use the improvements as an opportunity to demonstrate key elements of their programs, such as Metafore's display of interior applications of FSC certified wood, or creating an energy-efficient office design in the City of Portland's Office of Sustainable Development on the third floor. Other spaces highlighted artifacts from the original warehouse or showcased recent product developments in the green building industry. Each tenant went above and beyond the guiding principles of the building plan, to create spaces that are inviting, healthy, and vibrant. The results of the collective effort have far surpassed our original expectations. ■

—Eugénie Frerichs

keeping the half block for future redevelopment as the build-out of the River District increased land values and lease rates. Subsequently, our decision proved to be the right one as the City amended the zoning to provide building floor area and height bonuses on the property. This doubled the maximum height from 75 feet to 150 feet and substantially increased the floor area that could be built on the remaining half block.

Assembling the Building Team

We chose to develop the project using a negotiated bid process where the general contractor is selected at the start of the design process rather than by competitive bidding after the construction documents are finished. Typically historic rehabilitation projects are fraught with hidden conditions and unforeseen construction problems. We preferred to select an experienced and trusted contractor for the project versus taking the low bidder in a competitive bid situation. Having the contractor participate in the design process from the beginning also provided valuable feedback to the architect and to Ecotrust in terms of construction costs and the feasibility of the design. It is considerably cheaper to change things while they are still on paper than when they are in concrete and steel.

Ecotrust selected a young and energetic firm, Holst Architecture, to design the Natural Capital Center. Jeffrey Stuhr and John Holmes, the principals at Holst, had already designed successful conversions of existing warehouses in the River District — the Pacific Northwest College of Art and the RiverTec office building. Ecotrust paired Holst with Walsh Construction, one of the most experienced general contractors in Portland. Two green building consultants were added to the development team — Gregory Acker, a local architect specializing in sustainable design, and Ralph DiNola of Green Building Services, who coordinated our LEED™ certification (see Chapter 3). Carol Edelman and Breese Watson of Edelman Soljaga Watson designed the interiors of the public spaces and Ecotrust's offices.

Recruiting the Tenants

Early in the planning process we recruited tenants who shared our vision for the building and for the conservation economy. This ended up being very significant. Commitments from tenants helped secure financing, and the tenants helped shape the building design. Patagonia, Progressive Investment, Wild Salmon Center, the Certified Forest Products Council (now Metafore), Individual Tree Selection Management, and Shorebank Pacific all signed on before the design development phase was completed. The presence of Patagonia, which planned to build its first Portland store — its largest store to date — in the Natural Capital Center, gave the project instant credibility and opened many doors with city officials, lenders, and other tenants. As the design phase was not complete, we documented our agreement with these tenants with simple one-page letters of intent, referencing approximate space, location, and lease rates. These were then translated into formal leases as we developed the final building design.

The Design Process

Our directions to the architects were to stick with practical, low-tech, and no-tech solutions. We rejected green building technology that was experimental or not cost effective. We found that fuel cells were not yet practical or affordable, and that photovoltaics didn't make sense given the building's limited southern exposure. On the other hand, the latest high-efficiency office light fixtures worked well. Our goals for light, air, and water were translated into a design that incorporated skylights and an atrium to welcome natural light; operable windows and an air conditioning system to bring 100% outside air into the building for fresh air circulation; and an ecoroof, bioswales, and low-flow water fixtures to manage and conserve water. Sometimes we found ourselves trading one goal off against another. For example, we could have been even more energy efficient if we had replaced the old single-glazed windows with new double-glazed windows. Instead we chose to rebuild the original wood windows, maintaining the historic integrity of the old warehouse.

At each stage in the design, Walsh prepared a new cost estimate. As the estimates went up, we met with the developer, the architect, and the contractor to go through a painful process of reviewing the design and budget. Sometimes we stayed with the more expensive alternative. For example, in the rooftop addition we kept the post and beam construction using salvaged 100-year-old Douglas-fir timbers instead of a less expensive system using new lumber and lightweight trusses, but ended up with a much more interesting and inviting space. We also went to great lengths to keep the original Douglas-fir plank floors which give the building enormous character. This obligated tenants to refinish their floors rather than choose the cheaper but less interesting alternative of adding a new covering. The final construction contract price was $6.7 million (see The Project at a Glance on page 54 for a detailed breakdown).

The Portland Design Commission approved our design review application with minor changes. The plans were further refined and then submitted to the City for

The redeveloped offices on the second floor (bottom) attempted to preserve the open spans of the original warehouse (top).

MINIMIZING CONSTRUCTION WASTE

The redevelopment goal of salvaging as many materials as possible for reuse in the building and minimizing the amount of demolition and construction waste was greatly aided by the selection of Carrington Barrs as project manager by Walsh Construction Company, the project's general contractor. Barrs had recently finished his Masters work at the University of Washington in Construction Management with an emphasis on green building and was itching for a green building project. With Barr's leadership, the project achieved an unprecedented 98% rate for recycling construction waste, a record for the city of Portland, and well beyond Ecotrust's original goal of 75%.

RECYCLED & SALVAGED:

Material	Weight (tons)
Concrete	430.0
Land Clearing Debris	928.5
Wood	230.0
Gypsum Wallboard	80.0
Masonry	612.5
Cardboard	15.1
Steel	34.7
Furniture	0.5
Subtotal:	2,331.3

TO LANDFILL:

Material	Weight (tons)
Construction and Demolition Waste	57.4
Subtotal:	57.4
Total Waste to Landfill, Recycled & Salvaged:	**2,388.7**
Percentage of Recycled & Salvaged Construction Waste Material:	**98%**

The first priority was to reuse materials that came from the site itself, mainly from the deconstruction of an adjacent building, which yielded an ample supply of bricks, stone, and timber which was subsequently incorporated into the Natural Capital Center. The small surplus of materials were then donated or sold after the tenant improvements were completed.

The process of deconstructing, salvaging, sorting, reusing, or recycling any waste materials was guided by Barrs, with help from the ReBuilding Center in north Portland, which has extensive experience in salvaging materials that can be reused in other building projects. In anticipation of dissent from crew-members used to the standard three-day demolition of a building, Barrs offered clear instructions, consistent emphasis, and even day-end incentives for meeting the recycling goals. By the end of the project, as old timbers were transformed into new pieces of furniture or components in the building, and workers could see the fruits of their labor, most were sold on the idea and took pride in their contribution to the project.

Every month, Walsh Construction reported to the building team on the types of waste materials that were produced, the total quantity of waste and recyclable materials taken from the site, and the final destination of those materials. ■

—Eugénie Frerichs

a building permit. In addition to the typical construction documents, we added special green building sections to the project specifications. The tenant leases mandated green building practices and included a green building tenant improvement guideline (see **Tenant Improvement Guidelines** on page 50). While we developed the plans, we negotiated leases with the initial group of tenants, signed the final estimate and construction contract with Walsh, and secured construction financing from Bank of America.

Deconstruction and Reuse

While we were obtaining the permit for the redevelopment, we started work on deconstructing an adjacent building on the site under a separate permit. This building had been constructed after the original warehouse. It was built on rubble, with lower quality brick, and had significant structural problems. The careful deconstruction of this building yielded a treasure trove of materials for the redevelopment, including timbers for the rooftop addition, brick for the parapet repair, curbstones for benches, and gears and pulleys for table bases and other furniture. We established a "boneyard" to store this material for Ecotrust's future use and for use by our tenants. The convenience of the boneyard, located about ten blocks away, was a significant factor in stimulating the reuse of materials. All projects, from landscaping to tenant improvements, started with a visit to the boneyard for inspiration and an inventory of available materials.

Through a strong commitment and careful attention by our construction manager, Carrington Barrs, we were able to salvage and recycle an amazing amount of material that is usually considered construction waste — 98% by weight at final count (see **Minimizing Construction Waste** at left). Prior to starting the renovation, we also did a careful interior deconstruction, yielding a good inventory of tongue-and-groove paneling, interior doors, radiators, and other materials. Although much of the paneling was contaminated with lead paint, we were able to build attractive office partitions and wall coverings by exposing the unpainted side.

Redevelopment Highlights

The groundbreaking for the building took place on February 11, 2000. Layers of old grey paint were painstakingly stripped from the brick on the three historic façades of the building. Serendipitously, the paint also came off the concrete base of the building and the original stucco, restoring the building to its original

1895 appearance. As they worked on the brick façades, however, the masons soon discovered sections of the parapet walls where the mortar had essentially turned to sand. Eventually the entire parapet had to be taken down and rebuilt—an example of an unforeseen problem in historic rehabilitation work.

In order to bring the building up to the current seismic code (seismic zone 3), we constructed two steel towers on the west side of the building and structurally tied them to the building. Stairs were installed in both towers to provide access to the second and third floors. Because the building had been designed for a warehouse with heavy floor loads, the addition of a relatively lightweight 10,000 sq. ft. rooftop addition did not present a structural problem. A new interior structural steel frame was constructed to pick up the gravity loads from the entire structure and bring the building up to current codes. We removed a section of the second floor and installed a new skylight on the roof to bring daylight into the center of the first and second floors and to provide an open staircase between the first two levels.

We installed all new mechanical and electrical systems inside the building and added a new passenger elevator. As the construction progressed, we started the interior design of the common areas and Ecotrust's own space. Wherever possible, we recycled salvaged materials from the building back into the interiors. If that did not work, we used materials that were environmentally advantageous—from wood from well-managed forests to 100% recycled content sheetrock.

In the interior, we refinished the original wood plank floor, bearing the 100-year-old marks of the horse-drawn freight wagons that had driven over it for years. That meant nailing the plywood diaphragm required by the seismic code "upside down" on the underside of the first floor and experimenting with floor finishes that met our environmental goals and that would protect a soft wood in a commercial application.

Sometimes (but not often) we had pleasant surprises. When the contractor power-washed the roof trusses in preparation for painting them, we discovered that the 100-year-old paint washed away leaving the timbers looking like they were unfinished, new wood. Similarly, most of the lead-based paint on the interior brick walls washed away. The collected paint chips managed to fit into three garbage bags, a much better solution than the truckloads of lead-contaminated sand that sandblasting would have created.

A third floor was added using reclaimed posts and beams.

Steel towers erected on the western façade provide structural and seismic reinforcement.

THE PROJECT AT A GLANCE

The Building Team

Owner
Ecotrust Properties, LLC

Developer
Naito Development LLC

Architect
Holst Architecture P.C.

General Contractor
Walsh Construction Co.

Structural Engineer
KPFF Engineers

Mechanical/Electrical Engineers
Interface Engineering

Civil Engineer
KPFF Engineers

Interior Design
Edelman Soljaga Watson

Sustainability Consultant
Gregory Acker Architecture

Landscape Architect
Nevue Ngan Associates

LEED™ Consultant
PGE Green Building Services

Property Management
Ashforth Pacific, Inc.

Historic Consultant
Heritage Consulting Group

The Budget

	TOTAL	PER SF
Property acquisition	$ 2,500,000	$ 35.71
Hard Costs		
Construction contract	$ 6,672,217	$ 95.32
Change orders	431,541	6.16
Tenant improvements	1,242,921	17.76
Other	96,389	1.38
Subtotal	$ 10,943,068	$ 156.33
Soft Costs		
Architect & engineering	$ 676,706	$ 9.67
Green design fees & charette	82,579	1.18
Legal and accounting	85,000	1.21
Permits & fees	125,368	1.79
Developer fee	250,000	3.57
Pre-const. holding costs	100,387	1.43
Furniture, fixtures & equipment	35,500	0.51
Remaining contingency	133,564	1.91
Loan fees	66,000	0.94
Interest carry to breakeven	203,187	2.90
Leasing commissions	49,722	0.71
Other	78,919	1.13
Subtotal	$ 1,886,932	$ 26.96
Total:	**$ 12,830,000**	**$ 183.29**

Construction Contract

General requirements	$ 325,789
Site work	964,869
Concrete & masonry	782,295
Metals	1,126,973
Wood & plastics	646,468
Thermal & moisture protection	235,876
Doors & windows	376,547
Finishes, furnishings & specialties	451,984
Conveying systems	88,339
Mechanical	638,750
Electrical	418,800
Other	216,900
SUBTOTAL	$ 6,273,590
Contractor's liability insurance	$ 47,577
Contractor's overhead & profit	351,050
TOTAL	**$ 6,672,217**

Sources of Funds

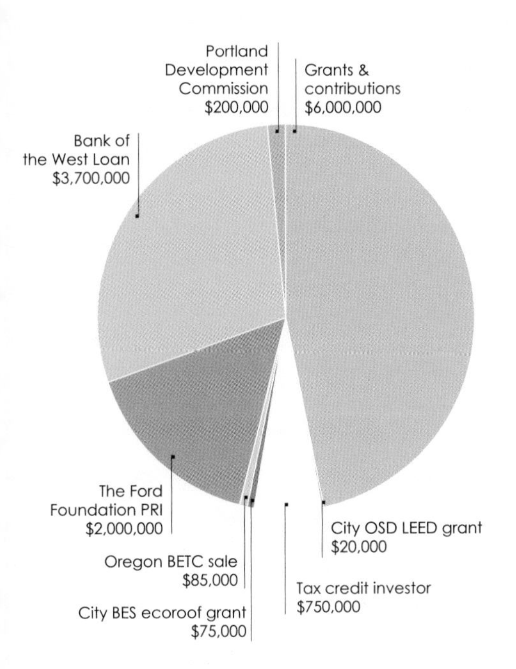

Building Program

Rooftop Addition **9,900 SF**
Office space: Metafore and City of Portland's Office of Sustainable Development; deck with fireplace, ecoroof

Second Floor **20,000 SF**
Office and conference facility; Ecotrust, Progressive Investment Management, Wild Salmon Center, and incubator space

Ground Floor **20,000 SF**
Retail space: Patagonia, Hot Lips Pizza, World Cup Coffee, ShoreBank Pacific, and Pearl Clinic and Pharmacy

Basement **20,000 SF**
Secure bicycle storage, locker rooms and showers, tenant storage

Site area **20,000 SF**
Seismic towers, loading dock, bioswales, 37 parking stalls, bicycle parking, truck loading, two car sharing stalls, electric vehicle charging station

ROOFTOP FLOOR PLAN

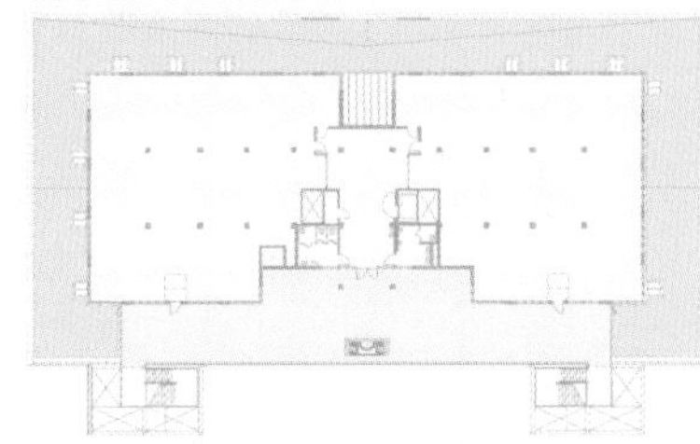

SECOND FLOOR PLAN

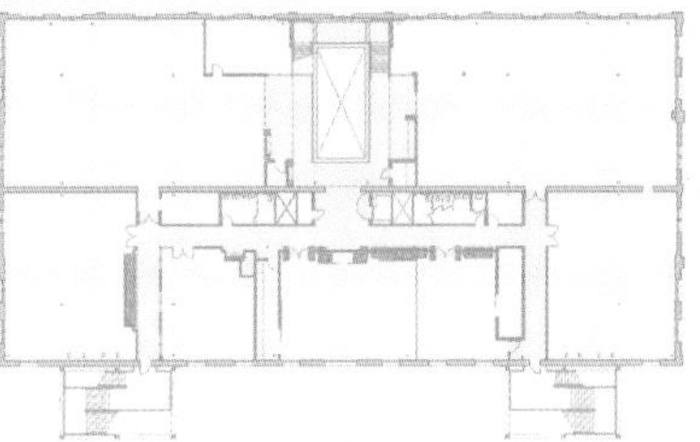

GROUND FLOOR PLAN

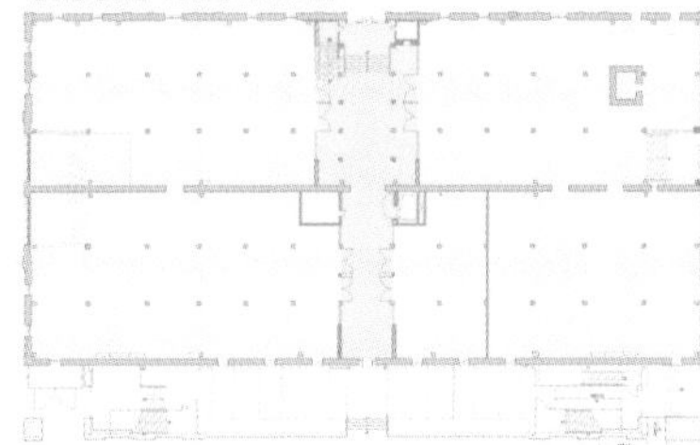

ELEVATION

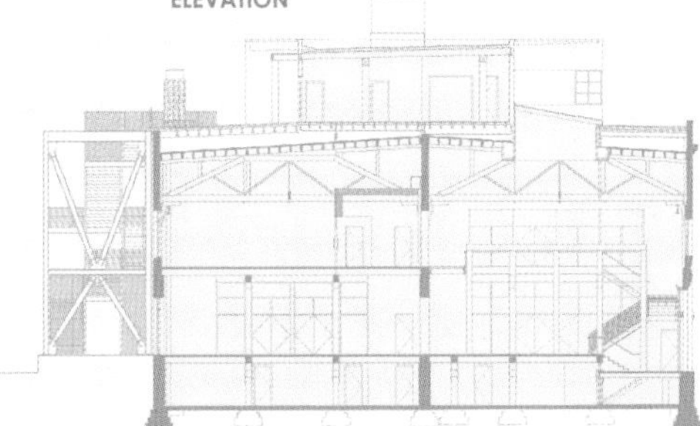

SO, HOW DID WE DO?

☑ **Create a center for the conservation economy:** With over 600 events in our conference center in the first 18 months, over 230,000 visitors, and a fully leased building of tenants doing cutting-edge work in the conservation economy, we are well on our way to meeting this goal.

☑ **Invite collaboration and build community among tenants:** Our first year has yielded wonderful collaborations and new partnerships. The retail tenants have partnered to create a collective identity and increase foot traffic. Ecotrust held a series of 20 lectures on the conservation economy to a full house, drawing on almost all of the tenants as guest faculty. Most importantly, we increased our sense of connection to each other, and to the collective goal of building a restorative economy and a just society.

☑ **Retain the building's historic character:** The building was preserved and the redevelopment followed national guidelines for historic redevelopment. We also managed to save and give new life to the historic interior features: the Douglas-fir floor planks, the interior brick, a walk-in safe, and the original wood windows, as well as using salvaged posts and beams for the third floor addition.

☑ **Incorporate green building:** The Natural Capital Center earned a gold LEED™ rating from the U.S. Green Building Council. Most significant is the extent to which this project stimulated the green building market. Our building team has gone on to design, develop, and engineer a number of green buildings. Ecotrust has given tours to thousands of planners, architects, engineers, builders, and developers, holding regular Wednesday tours as well as two or three more specialized tours each week.

☑ **Build a permanent headquarters for Ecotrust:** We did not anticipate the extent to which the Natural Capital Center would boost Ecotrust's local and national presence, but it has been a very welcome bonus. In terms of financial performance, we anticipated the building would generate approximately $340,000 in net cash flow (about 2.5% cash-on-cash return, or 5.5% on equity). The first year results, while positive, were significantly less, due primarily to the fact that the retail tenants were completing their tenant improvements and not paying rent. We also over-estimated the potential of the basement, which has limited clearance and no natural light. Going forward, we expect to generate $300-325,000 in net cash flow, considerably less than a commercial developer would demand, but sufficient for us given the programmatic returns and increase in underlying equity. ■

Financing

Ecotrust raised approximately $6 million in grants and contributions toward the $12.8 million purchase and construction of the Natural Capital Center, starting with a generous contribution from Ecotrust founding board member Jean Vollum. The redevelopment was financed with a conventional construction loan from the Bank of America. Once the building was occupied, we paid off the construction loan with permanent financing provided by the Bank of the West, the Portland Development Commission, and the Ford Foundation. The loan from the Ford Foundation is at a highly preferential rate of 1%; this below-market interest offsets Ecotrust's rent, allowing Ecotrust to occupy the building rent-free. The Ford Foundation, a long-time supporter of Ecotrust's programs and activities, chose this mechanism to permanently reduce Ecotrust's overhead and increase the flow of donations to programs. We gained additional equity from the sale of a federal historic tax credit and LEED state tax credit through Oregon's Office of Energy BETC program. The table and chart on pages 54–55 show the sources and uses of funds for the completed project.

Ecotrust benefited from grants, donations and some preferential loans due primarily to its charitable purpose and the intended public benefit of the Natural Capital Center. However, green building projects in general — whether public or private, residential or commercial — can also access preferential financing terms. For example, energy-efficient mortgages available to homeowners include lower energy costs along with other recurring payments such as principal, interest, and taxes. The energy-saving feature, such as extra insulation or better windows, is added to the principal and amortized over the life of the loan. Imagine a typical $100,000 mortgage with an $840 monthly payment and $90 in monthly energy bills. A $4,000 energy-saving feature that saves $40 in monthly energy expenses would lead to a $104,000 mortgage with a monthly payment of $868 and energy costs of $50 — a monthly cash benefit of $12. In addition, energy-efficient mortgages often qualify for a higher mortgage-to-income ratio, increasing buying power and helping additional borrowers qualify for loans.[2]

On the commercial side, lenders are concerned with the loan-to-value ratio (the amount of the loan as a percentage of the appraised value of the completed building) and the debt service coverage ratio (the annual cash flow generated by the building divided by principal and interest payments). Green building can help improve these important ratios through lower operating expenses, lower vacancy rates, faster recruitment of tenants, and lower risk of indoor air quality or hazardous materials issues. While recognition of these benefits is not universal, some progressive lenders are beginning to seek out and provide improved terms for green building projects.

Conclusion: Welcoming the Public

Celebrating the completion of an ambitious restoration project, Ecotrust welcomed tenants, civic leaders, and the public to a September 6, 2001, opening party at the Jean Vollum Natural Capital Center. Over a thousand people attended the event at which Portland Mayor Vera Katz, City Commissioner Dan Saltzman, and Patagonia founder Yvon Chouinard lauded the building as a great addition to the city and the region. Ecotrust obtained the certificate of occupancy only two days before the long-scheduled party, so the festivities were preceded by a mad rush to move in to the building. Ten minutes before the guests arrived, we stashed our packing boxes, put on our party smiles, gratefully accepted celebratory glasses of wine, and began the first of many building tours. ■

ENERGY

by Michael O'Brien, Erin Kellogg, and Bob Naito

The oil crisis of the 1970s focused most North Americans' attention on energy conservation, leading to some impressive, if often fleeting, gains in energy efficiency. Although we now know considerably more about the environmental toll of many of our conventional fuel sources — oil, coal, hydroelectric, and nuclear power — we have not progressed much farther in the use of renewable energy sources like solar, wind, and geothermal power beyond where we were three decades ago. Now, more than ever, energy conservation and a wholesale conversion to renewable energy sources are critical to the health of our planet. Not only is our energy consumption polluting the air and land, decimating wild fish runs, and creating waste that will continue to be toxic into our great, great grandchildren's lifetimes — it now threatens to alter the climate of the planet through the accumulation of greenhouse gases.

The construction and operation of buildings consumes about 30% of total energy use, creating significant opportunities for energy conservation and the expansion of renewable energy technologies. As a general rule, new buildings can achieve energy savings of 20% beyond what state regulations require with existing technologies and relatively modest investments with quick paybacks. If this easily achievable goal was widely implemented, the building sector could reduce overall energy use by 6%. This might, for example, allow the United States to eliminate imports of a significant amount of petroleum products from the Middle East. Achieving this 20% energy reduction goal was tougher for the Natural Capital Center than for most new buildings, given its orientation, high ceilings, historic features, and other factors.

Regardless of the obstacles, Ecotrust was committed to creating a building that would consume as little energy as possible, that was salmon friendly in its energy purchasing, that would be comfortable to work in, and that would provide excellent air quality and a feeling of control and responsibility for its occupants. The Natural Capital Center's building team evaluated a number of potential energy efficiency and renewable energy technologies, including raised floor systems, geothermal heat pumps, natural ventilation, solar panels, and fuel cells.

The new third floor is surrounded by an ecoroof and skylights which provide natural light to the second floor offices below.

THE REAL ENERGY SINK – GETTING THERE

Energy used by a building is only part of the whole story. In order for occupants and visitors to travel to and from the building, and for goods to be shipped in and out, transportation energy is also consumed. In fact, nationwide, transportation accounts for about 27% of total energy use, and in 2000, 87.5% of trips to work were by car.

MEANS OF TRANSPORTATION TO WORK, U.S. 2000 CENSUS

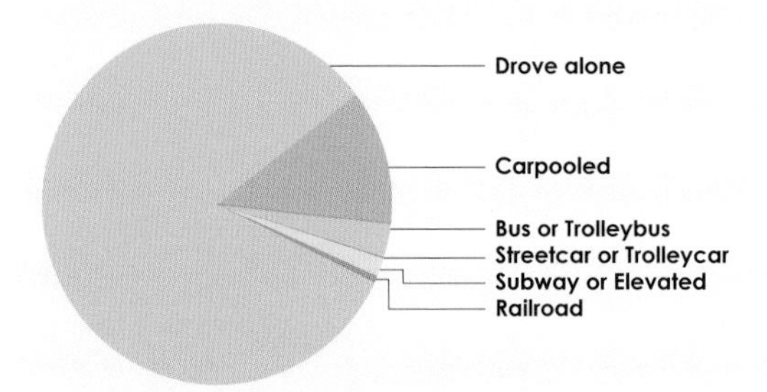

Source: U.S. Census Bureau, 2000 Census

In Oregon, transportation as a whole uses more energy than commercial buildings, accounting for 40% of the state's total energy consumption. In order to reduce total energy use, buildings must provide for alternative transportation. In the case of the Natural Capital Center, this includes:

- Location in the urban core with a variety of transportation alternatives and shorter trips to related businesses and organizations
- Location on the Portland Streetcar line for access to downtown core
- TriMet bike-bus capability for cyclists to commute by bus, MAX light rail, and streetcar
- Secure bicycle parking and storage on site
- Showers and lockers for bicyclists
- Partnership with Flexcar, a carsharing service, to have fleet vehicles accessible
- Organizational incentives, such as City of Portland subsidy of annual transit pass for building tenant Office of Sustainable Development (OSD) employees
- Organizational support for telecommuting
- Organization purchase of fuel-efficient hybrid vehicles, such as Hot Lips Pizza delivery and OSD fleet cars. ■

The Power to Conserve

In the United States, industrial uses and transportation consume the bulk of power — accounting for well over 50% of all energy used. Residential use accounts for another 19%. Commercial buildings presently consume the least amount of energy — 16% — but the area of commercial floor space and the energy use per square foot of that floor space continues to rise.[1] Commercial buildings typically use more electricity (though they only consume 16% of all energy, they account for 36% of all electricity use) so they are actually responsible for over 40% of all greenhouse gases because much of this electricity is generated by coal-fired plants.[2]

Fortunately, we wield the same degree of power to conserve energy as we do to consume it. Energy conservation is one of the most financially and environmentally rewarding ways to "green" a building project. The array of lower energy options and products to choose from grows daily. Conservation measures in buildings typically yield a 5–15% or more return on investment. Such low-risk rates of return are hard to find even among other investments like stocks and bonds.

In fact, power suppliers are finding that conservation is a better investment than new generation because it is reliable and less subject to abuses such as the energy pricing scandal that recently rocked California.

As of 1996, energy conservation efforts undertaken in the Pacific Northwest since 1980 resulted in cumulative annual conservation savings equal to about 1,000 megawatts, equivalent to the power output of five average-sized, gas-fired combustion turbines. The total retail value to consumers of electricity saved has been about $2.5 billion.

In addition to the ecological benefits, energy conservation also benefits local economies. When a homeowner spends money to weatherize his or her house, it creates jobs for local contractors and suppliers. When a homeowner spends dollars on fuels like electricity, natural gas, or oil, most of the money leaves the local economy. Fuel payments, for example, often go to pay debt service on revenue bonds for dams and power plants.

How Buildings Use Energy

When looking at opportunities for energy conservation in commercial building projects, it is helpful to first have an understanding of their energy use. As the accompanying chart illustrates, most of the energy — 45% — is dedicated to heating, cooling, and ventilation. Lighting consumes 18% and water heating another 13%. These systems are therefore the first and best ones to evaluate for energy efficiency.

It is also important to keep in mind that some of the highest energy use is not in the building itself, but related to the way people get to the building (see The Real Energy Sink — Getting There on opposite page). Any attempt to explore energy conservation in buildings should consider the following five key areas of opportunity:

- **On-site energy generation:** generating electrical energy directly from sunlight and wind, and using geothermal heat.
- **Efficiency:** reducing consumption of energy by improving the thermal envelope, heating and cooling system, daylighting, electric lighting, and equipment.
- **Embodied energy:** reducing the amount of energy embedded in the building itself, through deconstruction, salvage, reuse, and careful selection of new materials for high recycled content.
- **Green power:** purchasing electrical energy from renewable sources.
- **Transportation:** reducing energy used to transport people and goods to the building.

Another important point is that energy conservation is most effective when put in its proper local context. In the Pacific Northwest, buildings primarily use two types of energy: electricity and natural gas. A mix of hydroelectric dams, coal-burning steam generators, natural gas turbines, nuclear power plants, and biomass plants that burn wood chips or methane produce the bulk of the region's electricity. Renewable energy from wind, geothermal, and solar sources is still a small fraction of total energy production. The energy system in this region — Salmon Nation — is far from perfect. Hydroelectric power is particularly damaging to native wild fish populations, effectively preventing them from traveling to and from their spawning grounds in any sizeable numbers. Buildings and building owners, as energy consumers, should not underestimate their buying power and can help influence a dramatic shift in a region's energy plan. Concern about salmon populations, for example, has helped feed the demand for alternative energy sources like wind generation, which is a natural choice for the Columbia River Gorge along the Oregon and Washington border, a wind tunnel that draws wind surfers from around the world. Any strategy for conservation should first attempt to decrease overall energy consumption, then reduce the use of non-renewable and more environmentally harmful fuel sources, and increase the use of locally-available renewables.

A SNAPSHOT OF ENERGY USE IN COMMERCIAL BUILDINGS (YEAR 2000)

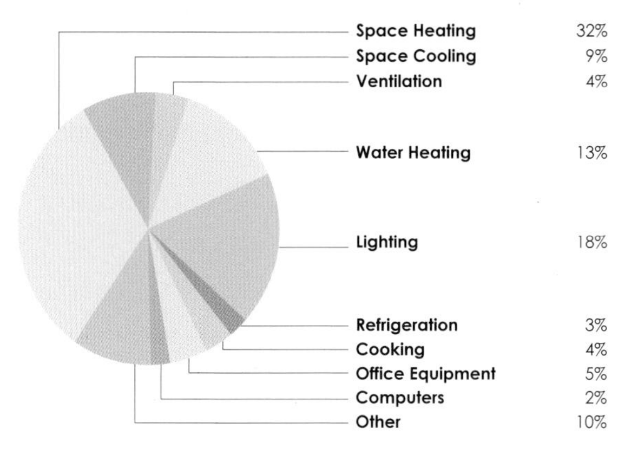

ENERGY USE IN COMMERCIAL BUILDINGS BY FUEL TYPE AND COST ($ BILLIONS/YEAR 2000)

Total: $111.8

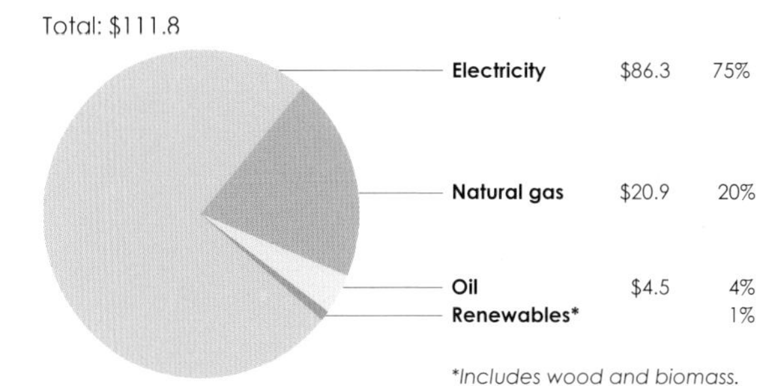

*Includes wood and biomass.

Source: Office of Energy Efficiency and Renewable Energy, *2002 Building Energy Database*, (Washington, D.C.: U.S. Department of Energy, July 26, 2002).

THE NORTHWEST POWER SYSTEM

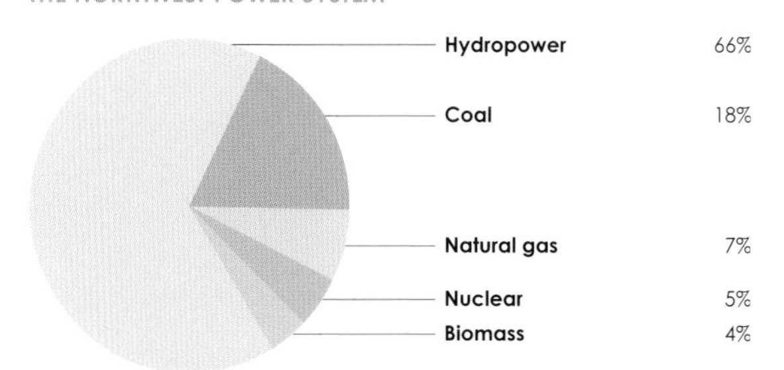

Source: Northwest Power Planning Council, *Revised Fourth Northwest Conservation and Electric Power Plan*, (Portland, OR: Northwest Power Planning Council, 2002).

KEY STEPS IN DESIGNING FOR ENERGY EFFICIENCY

Start early

If the project team waits until the design development or construction documents stage to think about energy efficiency, opportunities disappear and costs will increase. Start early, even if key players may not yet be selected or under contract. Set energy goals from the very beginning: In general, any new or renovated commercial building can improve performance by 20% compared to the building code using off-the-shelf technologies and strict cost budgeting.

Assign responsibility for meeting the energy goals: Designate one person to make sure the team addresses energy in all decisions affecting the building thermal envelope, space conditioning, day lighting, electric lighting and water heating.

Use modeling tools at the onset

Software programs like eQuest® make it possible to start modeling the energy performance of a building early in the design process. eQuest can be used by anyone familiar with building terminology, such as architects, engineers, or building managers. If energy modeling does not happen until the construction documents phase, it will be too late to include many cost-efficient measures. Modeling allows the team to identify and prioritize the most cost-effective measures quickly — that is, to understand how each energy measure improves performance compared to its cost. This builds confidence and commitment among team members. Modeling also allows team members to compare their efficiency targets to a "baseline" building that just meets minimum requirements set by building codes. These steps will help later in the process when the budget and design are reviewed occurs. Energy conservation measures are frequently cut when the project team does not fully understand them and lacks commitment.

Redefine economics

Using the conventional yardstick of "lowest first cost" to evaluate design and construction decisions usually results in buildings that dissatisfy occupants, cost more to operate, and consume too much energy. Commercial buildings are workplaces, and a good building supports the productivity and satisfaction of its occupants. Fortunately, design solutions that improve lighting, thermal comfort, and air quality are also the most energy efficient. The best solutions achieve high owner and occupant satisfaction at the lowest overall cost. ■

Designing Buildings for Energy Efficiency

Since every building is unique, achieving energy efficiency for each remodeling or renovation project requires a different approach. High-performance buildings — ones that save the most energy for the lowest investment — are the result of a team effort. When the building owner, developer, architect, mechanical engineer, electrical engineer, and general contractor collaborate in an integrated design process, a synergy takes place that leads to solutions appropriate for the building, the budget, and the occupants. (See **Key Steps in Designing for Energy Efficiency** at left.)

In a conventional renovation process, important players like the mechanical engineer and general contractor are not usually present during early planning and design. They are often put in the position of designing workable energy systems, without being able to influence key decisions. Energy efficiency can be difficult to achieve when later choices are constrained by earlier decisions.

Here is a common example: an architect specifies large areas of view glass facing east and west. One result will be to increase the need for air conditioning, to offset solar heat gains in mornings and afternoons. Another result may be to create thermal discomfort for occupants who sit next to the glass. Once the architect's choice of glass is incorporated into the plans and specifications, the die is cast. Subsequent decisions about cooling equipment will be driven by the cooling loads created by the glass type, area, and orientation.

In an integrated, team-based design process the mechanical engineer can give the architect immediate feedback about the consequences of such design decisions. He or she can show the team how keeping solar heat out of the building could save money on the initial cost of cooling equipment, reduce ongoing energy costs, and improve thermal comfort. Using today's fast and simplified computer energy modeling, the mechanical engineer can even quantify the savings.

With this information, the architect can specify special glass that rejects solar gains, and possibly reduce the area of the glass. These design changes will in turn cut the need for cooling and improve thermal comfort. The economic benefits are clear: the added cost of the special glass can be completely offset by lowering the initial cost of the air conditioning equipment, resulting in a building that is more comfortable for occupants and that consumes less energy over the years.

The Natural Capital Center's Approach

Ecotrust involved energy specialists in the initial stages of the Natural Capital Center redevelopment to ensure an integrated approach to energy systems design from day one. We began the project with high goals for energy conservation and indoor air quality, but had very little experience with energy systems and were not very familiar with the latest innovations in energy design. We knew we wanted to exceed current standards for energy efficiency and indoor air quality, but we didn't really know how. With these goals and very few preconceptions, we set out to do our homework, and with the entire building team explored every energy option that had the slightest potential for inclusion in the project.

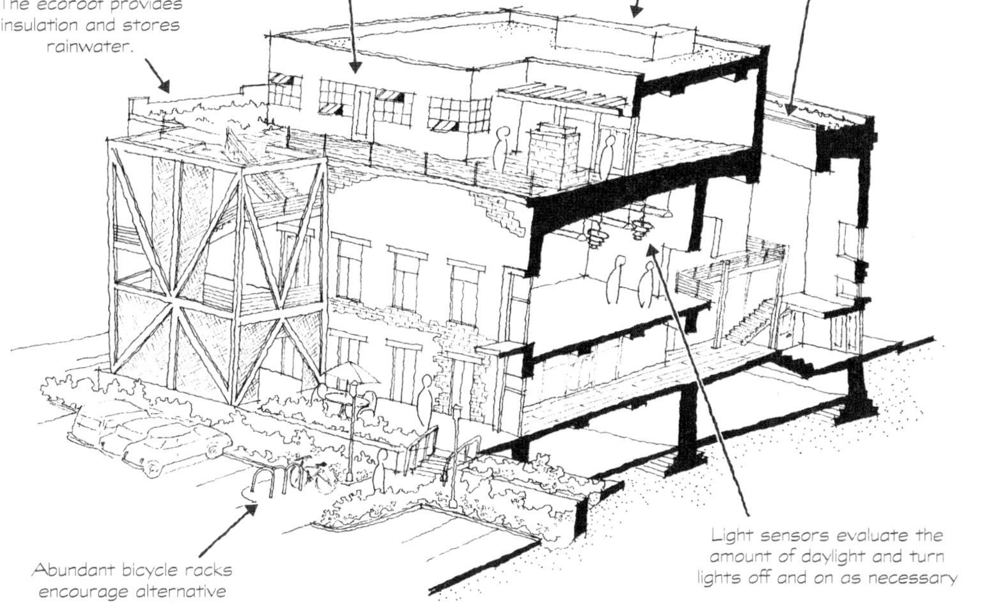

The first step was to understand our regional climatic patterns, in order to predict how the building, as an organism, would function in each season, and design energy strategies based on those patterns. Portland has a temperate climate where daytime temperatures are in the 50s in the winter and in the 80s in the summer. Nighttime temperatures in the summer typically fall into the 50s. Most commercial buildings in the region have air conditioning systems based on "terminal reheat." This means all the air coming into the building is cooled to the same temperature. The cooled air is sent to the different spaces in the building and reheated within each separate space to the appropriate comfort level. While it may seem grossly inefficient to cool air and then immediately reheat it, this system is used in the majority of commercial buildings today.

Given the inefficiency of terminal reheating, natural ventilation appealed to us, and we were willing to consider cutting air conditioning altogether. Knowing Portland's mild climate, we wondered how to make the building comfortable without air conditioning. We thought it might be possible by flushing the building with cool air at night (even summer nights are cool in Portland), and by letting occupants open windows. After much thought and analysis, we decided that we could not take this chance given the consequences of being wrong and the cost of adding air conditioning later.

ENERGY HIGHLIGHTS IN THE NATURAL CAPITAL CENTER

The variable air-volume heating and cooling system adapts to outside conditions to improve efficiency

New windows are highly energy efficient and operable, increasing flexibility and tenant control.

Skylights add natural light, reducing the need for lighting and improving productivity.

The ecoroof provides insulation and stores rainwater.

Abundant bicycle racks encourage alternative transportation.

Light sensors evaluate the amount of daylight and turn lights off and on as necessary

ENERGY HIGHLIGHTS IN THE NATURAL CAPITAL CENTER

A Sampling of the Natural Capital Center's Energy Conservation Measures

1. The atrium relies primarliy on natural light with a simple, low cost photocell, turning on lights when needed.
2. The entire building uses a dual fuel variable air volume (VAV) HVAC system so that gas heat provides a majority of the heating, while electric heat provides final zone heating. The VAV system provides added zone control and substantial fan energy savings over constant volume units, and takes advantage of the diversity of the building use.
3. The high-performance glass on the third floor reduces the HVAC unit size needed, improves comfort, and provides energy savings.
4. The HVAC system uses carbon dioxide sensors to prevent over-ventilation during low occupancy and save heating and cooling energy.
5. Occupancy sensors turn off lights when spaces are unoccupied, and signal the HVAC system to reset setpoints higher and lower until the space is occupied.
6. Artificial ambient lighting levels use the European standard of 30 foot candles (FC) as opposed to the U.S. standard of 50 FC.
7. Heating and cooling setpoints are set at 78°F for cooling and 68°F for heating, a much wider range than the usual 4°, to save heating and cooling energy.
8. The atrium has an even larger permissible temperature range, since it is a pass-through space, saving initial costs as well as heating and cooling energy.
9. Operable windows were installed (or refinished) to lessen the need for mechanical cooling.
10. Commissioning was performed by an outside professional to ensure that the building operates as efficiently as designed.

—Andy Frichtl, Interface Engineering

Units in individual workspaces reheat conditioned air to tenants' specifications.

Hot Lips Pizza Oven Heat Exchanger

Restauranteurs Dave Yudkin and Jeana Edelman, owners of Hot Lips Pizza, see their restaurants, the third of which opened its doors with the Natural Capital Center in 2001, not only as venues for fresh, local ingredients and creatively conceived menus, but as opportunities for innovation in fusing business with the environment. At their Natural Capital Center site, many of their ideas focused on energy solutions. For example, the oven is a bread oven typically found in bakeries rather than pizza joints. At twice the size of a conventional pizza oven, and with over 1,000 pounds of insulation lining the inside, the bread oven consumes half as much energy to bake larger volumes of pizza at one time. It is also equipped with a heat exchanger, which sends waste heat from the oven through a series of copper pipes to warm water that is fed into the hot water heater in the basement. The hot water is used for washing dishes and cleaning in the restaurant.

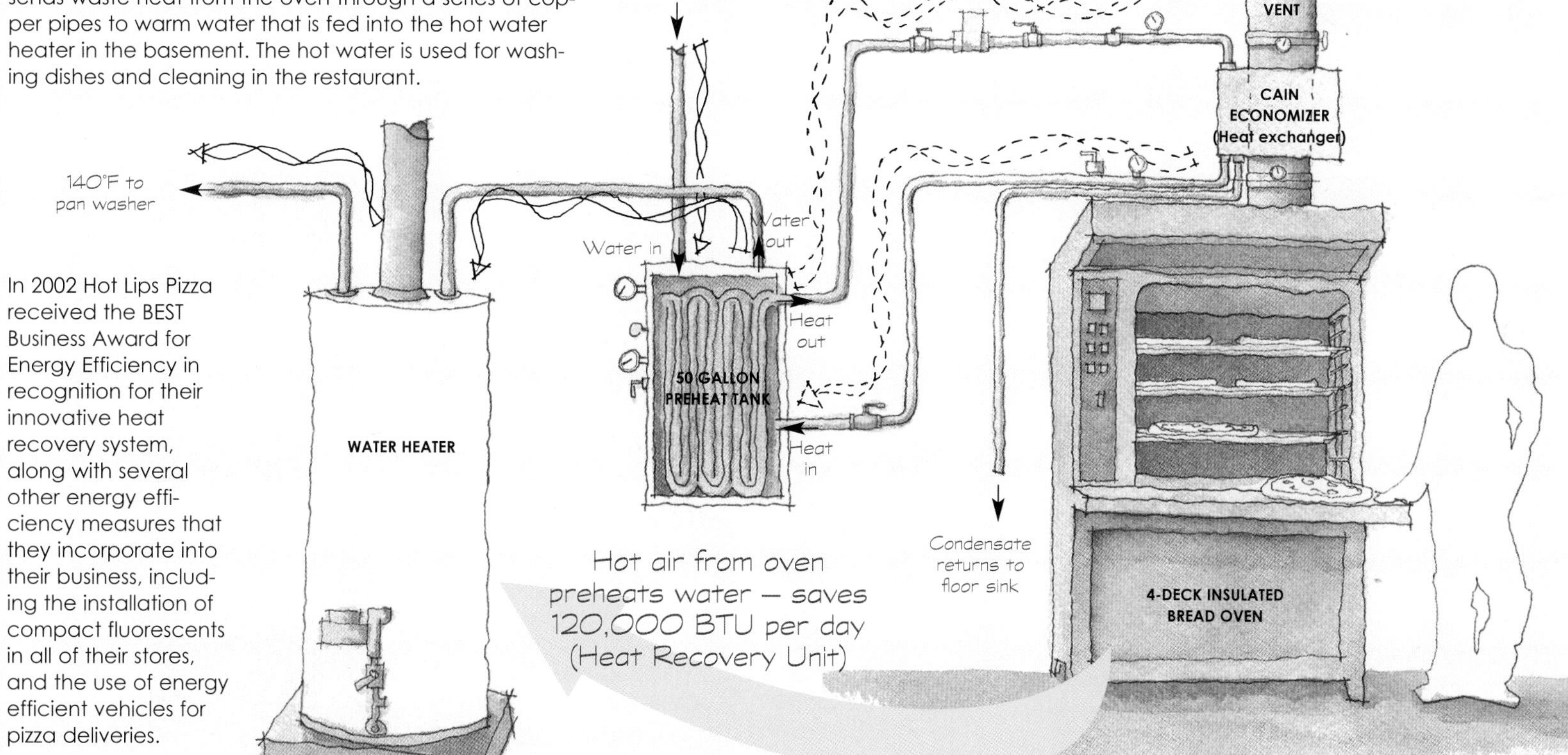

In 2002 Hot Lips Pizza received the BEST Business Award for Energy Efficiency in recognition for their innovative heat recovery system, along with several other energy efficiency measures that they incorporate into their business, including the installation of compact fluorescents in all of their stores, and the use of energy efficient vehicles for pizza deliveries.

FUEL CELLS: POLLUTION-FREE ENERGY?[3]

Fuel cells are a promising energy source that run on hydrogen — the most plentiful element found on Earth — and produce much fewer greenhouse gases or toxic emissions. A fuel cell operates like a battery, but as long as fuel is supplied it will produce energy in the form of electricity and heat without running down like a conventional battery.

As pictured below, it consists of two electrodes (an anode and a cathode) around an electrolyte. Oxygen passes over one electrode and hydrogen over the other to generate electricity, water, and heat.

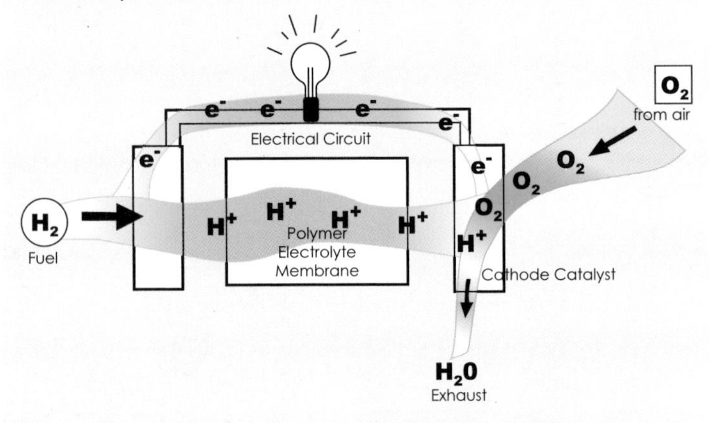

Source: Fuel Cells 2000 and the U.S. Department of Energy

The hydrogen used to power a fuel cell can come from many sources including water, methanol, ethanol, natural gas, gasoline, diesel or ammonia. Fuel cells can even run on gas from landfills and wastewater treatment plants, as several are today. There are currently nine different types of fuel cells with a variety of power generating capacities and different fuel sourcing abilities. Each is suited to a different application ranging from small computer devices to car and home use to industrial and energy utility use.

Fuel cells are already powering buses, boats, trains, planes, and bicycles, and all the major auto manufacturers are working to commercialize a fuel cell car. They can also be found powering vending machines, vacuum cleaners, and highway road signs. Over 200 fuel cell systems have been installed all over the world in hospitals, nursing homes, hotels, office buildings, schools, and utility power plants. Producing electricity at a higher efficiency than most other technologies, and creating only water and heat as waste products, they deserve to be seriously evaluated for any building project. ■

The architect initially proposed to cool the building with a "swamp cooler" that used no refrigeration. When this proved to be ineffective because of Portland's ambient humidity, the mechanical engineer proposed a conventional HVAC (heating, ventilation and air conditioning) system that is controlled by a computerized energy management system and that can bring 100% outside air into the building. This system mixes outside and internal air continuously to maintain a comfortable temperature inside the building. In the spring and fall, the system can bring outside air in to cool the building instead of running the air conditioning compressors in a form of "free cooling." On cool summer nights, the system can start up in the middle of the night to flush the hot air inside the building out and replace it with cool outside air.

The design team explored just as many options for heating systems. These decisions were more difficult. It is much harder to meet energy conservation requirements by retrofitting an existing building than it is with new construction. The LEED system recognizes this by awarding more points to retrofits. As described in Chapter 4, we had to make some trade-offs between energy conservation and historic restoration. In other instances, the orientation of the building precluded some options, while others that seemed appropriate at first later proved too expensive.

We gave serious consideration to using hot-water baseboard heat for higher energy efficiency and comfort, but we could not justify the lengthy payback period on the $400,000 system. We then asked the design team to take a hard look at adding a raised floor system on the upper floors. In a raised floor system, a new floor is installed 14"–18" above the existing floor. The entire space created under the raised floor becomes a low velocity duct for conditioned air. Each occupant has an operable floor vent that provides personal control of air flow and temperature at each workstation. The benefits of a raised floor system are vast, and include reduced energy costs, increased occupant comfort, and greater flexibility when it comes to future reconfiguration of the space. Unfortunately, a raised floor system proved to be too problematic in our building for several reasons. We wanted to retain the original Douglas-fir flooring on the first floor, and the windows on the second floor were so low to begin with that adding a raised floor would have lowered the windows to knee level. Furthermore, if we had installed a raised floor on the second floor while heating the first floor with a more conventional system, the mixed system would have been too complicated and too expensive. After much effort and thought, we concluded that such a system makes more sense when an entire building can be designed to take advantage of the raised floors.

We also explored some relatively radical energy solutions. We considered installing a geothermal heat pump that would use the earth's mass to provide heating and cooling. A geothermal heat pump circulates refrigerant through pipes buried in the ground. The heat pump exchanges heat between the building and the earth, much in the way that air conditioners exchange heat between a building and the air; geothermal pumps, however, are far more energy efficient. They achieve efficiencies of 150% and higher because they move more heat-energy than they consume in electrical energy. Also, because the earth's temperatures are steady, compared to air temperatures, geothermal heat pumps can be much more reliable and better matched to a building's heating and cooling needs.

For the Natural Capital Center, such a heat pump would have required digging deep holes into the ground for the pipes that circulate the refrigerant. The wells would have been expensive and would have conflicted with the soon-to-be installed seismic bracing system. Again, we had to look elsewhere for energy efficiency. We considered using fuel cells to provide emergency power to the building in the event of a power failure and decided that this did not make sense given the expense and regulatory issues they would have entailed. We also briefly considered working with photovoltaics but were again discouraged by their cost and payback, given the orientation of the building and the competing uses of the roof for water filtration and storage.

Before making any final decisions about installing a heating and cooling system, we tested a design for the Natural Capital Center using the DOE II (Department of Energy) computer modeling system to see if our design would exceed energy codes. Not satisfied with the results of the modeling, our developer Bob Naito made one last ditch effort and asked the mechanical engineer to evaluate a water-source heat pump system. This system had the virtue of capturing heat generated by the lights, computers, and people in the building. In a larger footprint building, this type of HVAC system would have been more energy efficient, but again, it did not make sense in ours.

After months of research and several dead ends, having exhausted many of the more pioneering, whole-systems options, we chose to install natural gas-fired warm-up boilers that temper the air during a morning warm-up cycle, and provide most of the heat for the building. During the day, if more heat is called for at the perimeter of the building, electric resistance heaters at terminal units kick in. The system is pre-set at 78°F for cooling and 68°F for heating, a temperature range that is broader than in most conventional buildings. Tenants can open windows or put on and take off layers of clothing to adjust their own levels of comfort.

The historic windows on the second floor were refinished and retained, often with their original century-old glass panes.

GREENHOUSE GAS REDUCTION INITIATIVE

Under the leadership of Indigo Teiwes-Cain, research analyst for Progressive Investment Management and chair of the building's energy working group, the tenants of the Natural Capital Center joined forces in 2002 to reduce the energy footprint of the Natural Capital Center by 90% through a two-pronged strategy: a purchase of "green tags" from the Bonneville Environmental Foundation and the purchase of carbon offsets from the Climate Trust.

The group of tenants will reduce their CO_2 emissions by purchasing 25% of their electricity from wind power through the Bonneville Environmental Foundation's Green Tags program. BEF Green Tags come from new wind and solar resources. One Green Tag equals the production of one megawatt hour of renewable, non-polluting electricity and offsets 1,400 pounds of emissions. The net revenue from selling BEF Green Tags is invested in the next new renewable energy project.

Tenants also donated funds to the Climate Trust to help an Oregon project that improves the energy efficiency of apartments and commercial buildings. The agreement will enable The Climate Trust to expand its project with Portland's Office of Sustainable Development to work with the owners of over 12,000 apartment units and about 40 commercial buildings statewide to improve energy efficiency.

The long-term goal of the Natural Capital Center's energy working group is to reduce the building's energy footprint as much as possible. In future years, the group will tackle indirect forms of energy use, such as transportation and travel, as well as the direct energy use addressed in 2002. In addition, the group will continue to evaluate the addition of fuel cells, solar panels, and other technologies to the building, as well as continuing investments in energy efficiency. ■

FIGHTING CO_2 HERE AND THERE

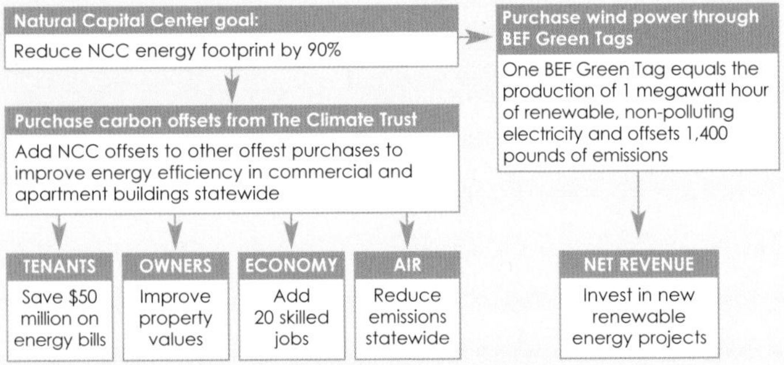

Natural Capital Center goal:
Reduce NCC energy footprint by 90%

Purchase carbon offsets from The Climate Trust
Add NCC offsets to other offest purchases to improve energy efficiency in commercial and apartment buildings statewide

TENANTS	OWNERS	ECONOMY	AIR
Save $50 million on energy bills	Improve property values	Add 20 skilled jobs	Reduce emissions statewide

Purchase wind power through BEF Green Tags
One BEF Green Tag equals the production of 1 megawatt hour of renewable, non-polluting electricity and offsets 1,400 pounds of emissions

NET REVENUE
Invest in new renewable energy projects

—Indigo Teiwes-Cain and Bettina von Hagen

We also found that certain energy options, when used throughout the entire building, contributed greatly to overall efficiency. For example, all office lighting fixtures use T-5 High Output bulbs, the most efficient available. We used the European standard of 30 **foot candles (FC)** as opposed to the U.S. standard of 50 FC for artificial ambient light levels. Occupancy sensors in hallways, closets, restrooms, and meeting spaces turn off lights when spaces are empty and signal the heating and cooling system to reset the thermostat higher or lower until the space is reoccupied. Finally, we relied heavily on daylighting, or the use of natural light, throughout the building in order to lower the demand for electrical lights during the day. All workspaces and areas of high traffic are oriented around the perimeter of the building, where windows and skylights provide ample natural light. Areas that are used with less frequency or for shorter periods of time, such as closets, restrooms, and supply rooms, are in the center of the building and are equipped with occupancy sensors. Large skylights were added throughout the second floor. The largest skylight, which sheds light into the first-floor atrium throughout the day, is surrounded by lights that are equipped with photovoltaic sensors. When there is plenty of natural light, the electric lights shut off, and when it grows dim outside, the sensors switch the lights back on. (See Energy Highlights in the Natural Capital Center on page 64.)

Foot candles (FC) are a unit of measurement that describes the light output of a source of light per square foot. The term was first used to describe a standard candle's illumination of surfaces that were one foot away. 100 foot candles is generally considered enough light to perform most tasks.

Recognizing that the most profound impact we (or any building) can have will only come from altering the building's energy supply at the source, we created a Greenhouse Gas Reduction Initiative (see sidebar at left), through which tenants voluntarily commit to purchasing renewable energy and offsetting greenhouse gas emissions. Energy-efficient design can help to conserve resources, but in the long run this only serves to make buildings "less bad" and should be coupled with more radical shifts, like finding renewable energy sources.

The Power of Air: Natural Ventilation

When the building team researched the use of natural ventilation to maintain thermal comfort in the Natural Capital Center, we wanted tenants to open and close their windows, and for the mechanical ventilation to bring in outside air, without air conditioning and space heating. Eliminating these features would have saved about 40% of the total energy used in the building. We were stymied by uncertainty — would natural ventilation keep the building within acceptable temperature and humidity ranges for us and for our tenants?

Recently, Portland architecture and mechanical engineering firms have begun to use a design technique developed in Europe to better understand natural ventilation, called computational fluid dynamics (CFD). Using this tool, designers can visualize the dynamic flow of air and temperatures through a building. In the hands of a trained user, this graphic modeling technique literally paints a picture of the building over a year of seasonal weather changes and outdoor conditions. The designer can see airflows and how changes in the design, such as window placements, affect thermal comfort. CFD is one of the only simulations that can provide the design team the assurance it needs that a building will operate as expected.

In the mild maritime climate of the Pacific Northwest, for example, CFD analysis shows that natural ventilation is practical in a wide variety of buildings. A few projects — North Clackamas High School, West Salem High School, and Washington School for the Deaf — have already incorporated natural ventilation in their design.

Even though evidence is mounting in favor of natural ventilation in buildings, it is still difficult for many developers to specify this approach in their plans. Experts in building technologies tend to know about a few things in great depth, since one of their main responsibilities is to build buildings that work properly and do not injure anyone, at the lowest possible cost. They tend to repeat their successes, because trying out new technologies always carries some risk of unanticipated problems or failures. Even accomplished professionals have difficulty staying abreast of new technologies and gaining the confidence to install them in buildings. Using natural cooling and ventilation means trying something that is still unfamiliar to many of today's professionals.

COMMON NATURAL VENTILATION STRATEGIES

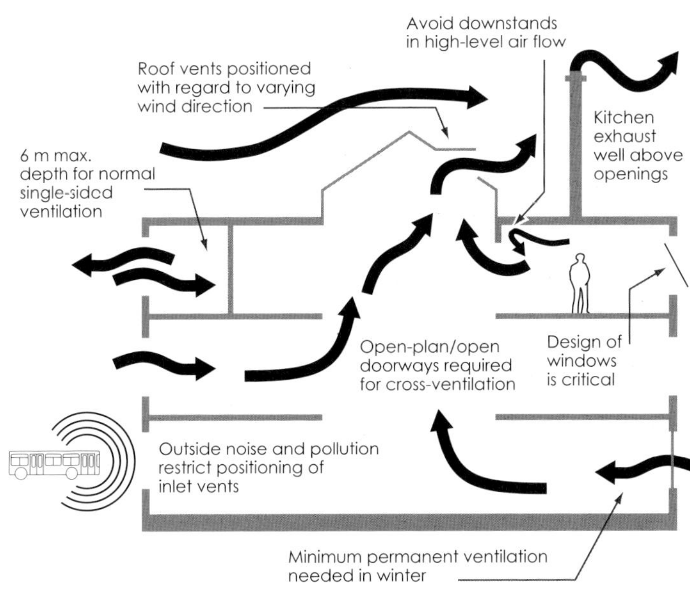

Source: Ian Theaker, P.Eng. (Interface Engineering) and Paul Schwer, P.E. (PAE Consulting Engineering).[4]

VI

COOLING DOWN THE HEAT ISLAND EFFECT

In addition to their contributions to watershed health, green roofs also work to reduce the "urban heat island effect." This modern phenomenon has emerged with the dramatic decline in vegetative cover in the urban landscape. Asphalt parking lots have replaced green space, and paved streets, sidewalks, and bare rooftops absorb solar energy and release it as heat, raising urban temperatures by as much as 10°F.

The rise in city temperatures leads to increased energy consumption from cranked up air conditioners that send out exhaust in the form of warmed air, increasing city temperatures even more. Fossil fuel consumption rises, which increases greenhouse gases and smog. Hot air and smog draw people indoors, where they turn up air conditioners. If left unchecked, the heat island effect can make the urban experience during summer months extremely uncomfortable, and even dangerous, to people and natural systems alike.

Recent studies show that widespread use of green roofs can help to bring these temperatures back down, by covering rooftops with soil and plants instead of black tar, retaining moisture in the soil, releasing moisture into the atmosphere through evapotranspiration, creating a buffer between the roofing membrane and the sun, and insulating the building. Cooled rooftops also lead to cooler stormwater runoff, which is beneficial for aquatic species (especially salmonids) in local waterways.

In Chicago, where summer temperatures have elevated to alarming levels in recent years, the local government has covered its City Hall with one-half green roof, one-half conventional roof. Researchers monitor and compare the temperature variations between the two roofing strategies, speculating that green roofs may be a solution to Chicago's pressing heat island effect. Early studies reveal promising results: Thus far, researchers have found that temperatures on the City Hall green roof are on average 25 to 80°F cooler than the conventional roof over the county office building next door.[5]

With help from non-profits and green roof advocates around the world, similar studies are cropping up in Tokyo, New York, Portland, and Philadelphia, to name a few. Their success at reducing the heat island effect will depend on the widespread use of green roofs as a building strategy, since acres of vegetative cover will more dramatically impact city temperatures than a few thousand square feet. Yet individual projects, such as the Natural Capital Center or Chicago's City Hall, are a critical first step, providing proof and recommendations for a building strategy that could quickly become a common way to cool things down. ■

—Eugénie Frerichs

Experience is proving, however, that building occupants actually prefer natural ventilation to mechanical ventilation, even when thermal comfort is not ideal. Mechanical engineers have researched thermal comfort and defined acceptable comfort in a series of standards published by ASHRAE, the American Society of Heating, Refrigeration and Air Conditioning Engineers. The standard defines a thermal comfort "envelope;" that is, the range of temperatures and relative humidity that most people find comfortable. Actually, the standard says that 80% of building occupants will be satisfied — it is not possible to achieve 100% satisfaction. Humans are too variable and their preferences change over time. Even the type of clothing a person wears affects their perception of comfort. For example, wearing light clothing in summer may cause people to feel too cool in an air-conditioned building. Researchers have documented that people like being able to open a window and to adjust thermal comfort in their personal space so much that they will accept less comfort in exchange for more control. Air coming in an open window might be cooler than the standard specifies, yet feel fresh and bracing to the occupant.

Mechanical engineers are beginning to revise their standards to acknowledge this preference. Hopefully, this change will help make natural ventilation more acceptable to engineers and building designers — thereby saving a tremendous amount of energy that would otherwise be used in heating and cooling.

A building's internal temperature control system affects not only the comfort of its occupants but those outside the building as well. A cluster of mechanically ventilated buildings with conventional roofs can elevate the temperature of an entire neighborhood or city in what is called the "heat island effect." Green roofs are a very effective way to mitigate this problem. This is explained in greater detail in Cooling Down the Heat Island Effect (see sidebar at left).

The Power of People: Monitoring and Feedback

One of the largest variables in building energy use is the occupants' behavior. In a conventional building, occupants often do not or cannot control energy-using equipment. When occupants do have controls for air conditioning, heating, lighting, and equipment they can and will learn to use the controls to minimize energy use — if they get feedback. When people know how much energy they use, and can see the savings that follow from their actions, they usually will conserve. Most buildings, however, do not provide any feedback. There is typically only one electric and gas meter for an entire building, even though there are many separate tenants. At a minimum, each tenant needs to be metered, in order to understand how much energy they use, what it costs, and how they can conserve and save money.

The main reason that metering equipment is not installed in every space is the significant extra expense to the building owner. Today's metering equipment is also not very user-friendly, and not easily understood by lay people.

Fortunately, buildings themselves are becoming smarter and better able to tell occupants about their energy use, yet in most cases this capability is not used. Many new buildings have control systems that connect a central computer to every component in the air conditioning, heating, lighting, security, and fire safety systems. Such a computer is capable of generating detailed reports on energy use. A common barrier to accessing this information is lack of training for the building operator who manages the computer, and turnover in staffing that brings in new people unfamiliar with the computer's capabilities.

The Power of Buildings: Creating Energy On Site

Most of the talk about alternative energy sources — switching from electricity to natural gas or buying Salmon Friendly Power — or even energy conservation measures, is merely fiddling at the margins. The ultimate in energy-efficient design is a building that generates its own power on site. Such a building would capture sunlight and turn it into electricity with **solar photovoltaic** panels. It would use heat pumps to exchange heat from the building to the earth's mass for cooling and heating, an idea that has in fact been around for many years.

> **Solar photovoltaic** electricity is generated by sunlight falling on panels made of special silicon, like the material in computer memory chips. The panels typically turn about 10% of available sunlight into electricity.

So why aren't all new buildings doing this already? What are the real barriers? Some obstacles may simply be social barriers, lack of information, or lack of familiarity with what is technically possible. Take, for example, Portland's Commonwealth Building, the first commercial building in the United States to install geothermal heat pumps, sealed double-paned windows, and heat recovery ventilation — all in 1948. The heat pumps were recently renovated after more than 55 years of service. That a building in Portland has been using geothermal heat pumps successfully for over 50 years speaks to the core of most obstacles to green building: the barriers are not so much technical as social and educational.

But there are also legitimate technical reservations. For example, does enough sunlight really fall on a building to provide energy for all its power? This question has been explored by a group of Portland design professionals. According to initial analysis, a combination of conservation and solar electricity could be suffi-

Solar photovoltaic panels on the Brewery Blocks redevelopment take advantage of the building's southern exposure.

STIMULATING GREEN BUILDING THROUGH TAX CREDITS

The Oregon Office of Energy offers a Business Energy Tax Credit (BETC) for investments in renewable energy, co-generation energy efficiency, development of markets for recycled products, and transportation.[6] The tax credit is 35% of the incremental cost of the system or equipment that is beyond standard practice. To date, more than 5,500 Oregon energy tax credits have been awarded. Altogether, these investments save or generate energy worth about $100 million a year.

In 2001, a sustainable building tax credit was added to the program. To obtain the credit, the building applicant must meet the Silver standard set by the U.S. Green Building Council's Leadership in Energy and Environmental Design (LEED). The credit amount is based on the square footage of the entire building and helps offset the cost of applying for the LEED rating and the extra design and commissioning costs. In addition to the credit requirements for the LEED Silver rating, the Office of Energy requires additional commissioning, a report on the amount of solar radiation to be received by the building annually, and that at least two LEED credits are earned for energy efficiency.

In 2002, the Natural Capital Center, taking advantage of the program's pass-through option which allows the sale of the energy tax credit to a tax-paying entity, sold its LEED tax credit to Walsh Construction, its general contractor. Ecotrust's eligible project costs, based on square footage and a Gold LEED rating, were $321,700. Walsh Construction paid Ecotrust $86,859, the net present value of the credit. The 35% tax credit of $112,595 was issued to Walsh Construction. The receipts from the tax credit sale covered Ecotrust's costs of commissioning and LEED certification.

The solar income calculation required to obtain the BETC sustainable building tax credit was developed to assess the capacity of Oregon buildings to capture solar energy. As described in the text of this chapter, buildings have the potential to generate all of their own power on site, especially if zoning and building codes anticipate and plan for maximizing solar exposure. The Natural Capital Center was the first building to be assessed for its solar potential under this program. Despite the north-south orientation of the building and extensive shading from surrounding buildings, the Natural Capital Center has the potential to generate 35% of its annual energy usage from solar energy. ■

— Bettina von Hagen

cient for many types of buildings. As described in the chart below, *Solar Income and Energy Use*, only tall office buildings would have to import energy. There would still be practical obstacles, such as the initial cost of a full photovoltaic system, and integrating solar modules into a building. However, the short answer is that yes, it really is possible. As a case in point, a building not far from the Natural Capital Center was recently constructed with solar photovoltaic panels on the entire south façade and rooftop. As part of the process to earn the Oregon Office of Energy's Business Energy Tax Credit (BETC), the Natural Capital Center underwent the same analysis and found that it has the potential to generate 35% of its annual energy usage from the sun. (See **Stimulating Green Building Through Tax Credits** at left.)

SOLAR INCOME AND ENERGY USE

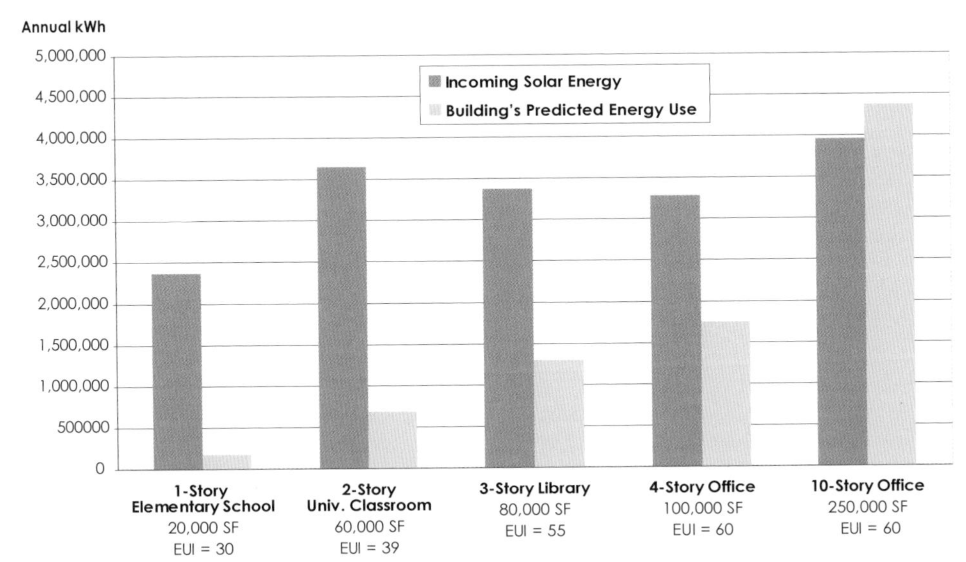

Notes:

1. The annual kWh of incoming solar energy is based on the amount of solar radiation incident on the roof and south façade of a building in Portland, OR.
2. The calculation of incoming solar energy assumes that the roof is 5% shaded, and the south façade is 30% glazed and 20% shaded.
3. Current PV technology can convert approximately 10–15% of the incoming solar energy shown above into electrical energy.
4. The Building's Predicted Energy Use assumes an energy efficient building that uses approximately 30% less energy than other buildings in its class. This is easily achievable with energy conservation measures.
5. The EUI, or Energy Use Index of a building, is used to compare the energy performance of buildings that vary in size. The EUI is expressed in kBtu/sq.ft./yr.—the annual energy use in btus divided by the total area of the building in square feet. The EUIs listed here are based on a 30% reduction of the average EUI for each respective building type.

Source: PAE Consulting Engineers, Inc., Portland, Oregon; www.pae-engineers.com.

Lastly, there is the matter of economics, probably the single most stated reason for opting out of energy efficiency. Yet there is one extremely significant, often overlooked reason to generate power on site. When buildings use energy produced somewhere else, there is a little-known energy accounting problem. Electricity for the Natural Capital Center, for example, is generated at dams, fossil fuel plants, and nuclear reactors throughout the Pacific Northwest. This electricity is transported by a high-voltage transmission system where fully two-thirds escapes as heat. In other words, three kilowatts of electricity must be generated to get one kilowatt to the building. By comparison, almost all the energy generated by a building's solar panels can be used on-site. Using standard energy accounting, solar panels would be rated 30% efficient, rather than the customary 10%, as no energy is lost during transmission.

Conclusion

Energy conservation is one of the most satisfying strategies in greening a building, as it offers the most dramatic financial paybacks as well as rewards in occupant comfort. Nonetheless, designing for the highest level of energy efficiency is a complex and often humbling undertaking. Lofty goals are often whittled down in the face of financial realities, operational constraints, and competing priorities. But as more and more buildings strive for higher energy performance, renewable energy and energy-efficiency technologies will become more widely available and less expensive, and goals once difficult to attain will fall easily within the reach of most building projects. ■

WATER

by Eugénie Frerichs

It is hardly a surprise that the communities of the Pacific Northwest have begun to implement many of the newest strategies for integrating water and the built environment. Cities throughout this bioregion receive an average annual rainfall of thirty-seven to forty-six inches. In other words, it rains a lot here, a fact that, for better or worse, generates conversation. Water influences every aspect of daily life. It seeps into the work of local artists, engineers, educators, and city officials. It inspires, challenges, and harasses, and ultimately, in its presence or absence, water prevails.

Learning From the Past

About a mile due south of the Natural Capital Center as the crow flies, at the King's Hill bus stop, the following words are engraved in stone:

> "In the eons before the city, a creek flowed where you are standing. It descended out of the hills to the west, through alder and hemlock groves to the Willamette River. The creek provided for animals and indigenous inhabitants, like any stream... As the 20th century began, Tanner Creek was buried under tons of fill and entombed in brick and concrete pipes because it had become a nuisance to encroaching urbanites. In its natural state, it flowed over impermeable clay and basalt and flooded nearby roads during torrential rains. Now it winds far below the city, hidden, forty feet beneath this very spot. Its path can still be traced by the cracked facades of some of the buildings above it."[1]

From southwest Portland, the relentless but still-buried Tanner Creek continues, winding its way north through the city until, just before flowing into the Willamette River, it passes directly underneath the Natural Capital Center. There the creek has made its presence known, with little subtlety, its course leading to a complete demolition of the building across the street, whose foundations had settled so much that cracks had woven their way up the entire façade. The Natural Capital Center narrowly escaped a similar fate: the redevelopment project included structural work to accommodate settling in some areas above the creek's path.

After a century of funneling natural waterways, stormwater, and sewage through the city's underground maze of pipes, Portland has achieved nothing less than seasonal floods, clogged drains, and raw sewage overflowing annually into a Willamette River that is polluted, eroding at its banks, and foggy with suspended

STORMWATER POLLUTANTS: THE SHORT LIST[2]

Suspended solids

Soil and dust particles, windswept or from erosion are a major concern in the Pacific Northwest, where siltation affects spawning Pacific salmon.

Nutrients

Nitrogen and phosphorous from lawn and garden fertilizers or pet excrement leads to entrophication (algae growth) in water, which depletes oxygen for native aquatic plants.

Bacteria

Commonly found at high levels in stormwater, includes fecal coliform.

Hydrocarbons

Engine oil, gasoline and diesel fuel from roads and parking lots is toxic to aquatic flora and fauna.

Trace metals

Lead, zinc, cadmium, copper, and mercury from atmosphere, car tires, and fluids. Some metals (mercury) can build up in the food chain in aquatic species and reach toxic levels for humans. Copper, highly toxic to aquatic species, has become the most abundant metal in stormwater, coming from the brake lining in cars.

Pesticides

From landscaping and agriculture are toxic to aquatic species.

Chlorides

From salts applied to roadways in winter weather dissolve and flow into surface water, drastically increasing the salinity.

Trash and debris

More of an eyesore, trash and debris can carry other pollutants with it into waterways, and also clog street drains, increasing small-scale flooding.

Thermal pollution

Pavement and flat roofs that are heated by the sun increase the temperature of water that flows over the surface. The warm runoff then heats the nearby waterways, and is harmful to cold-water fish such as Pacific salmon. ■

solids. The process is so consistent that every year during the rainy season, the Willamette River receives a steady barrage of "combined sewer overflows," or CSO's, which occur when the volume of stormwater overwhelms the city's sewage treatment facilities. A rainstorm in Portland is akin to a mini-flashflood. With every storm, overburdened sewer pipes send a cascade of fresh water from submerged creeks and streams, sanitary sewage, and runoff from parking lots, sidewalks, city streets, and rooftops directly into the river. This soupy flood is rich with contaminants (see **Stormwater Pollutants: The Short List** at left) and elevated in temperature after flowing over warmer impermeable surfaces. The recipient of these overflows is a river with severely degraded habitat for aquatic flora and fauna, and that is somewhat of an embarrassment for a city often hailed as one of the most environmentally progressive in North America.

As a result, the City of Portland is spending an estimated $30 million on the Tanner Creek Stream Diversion Project. This multi-phase project — which is one small part of a twenty-year, billion dollar stormwater management plan — will separate Tanner Creek and other stream flows from the city's sewer pipes by installing an underground pipeline that will carry the clean water directly to the river, circumventing the sewer system altogether. By 2011, Portland's Bureau of Environmental Services hopes to reduce overflows to the Willamette River by an average of 165 million gallons a year, achieving an overall reduction rate of 94%.[3]

The Tanner Creek Stream Diversion Project is far from an ideal solution. Rather, it is an expensive, temporary fix to a problem that started many years ago, when the city first attempted to divert water using the fastest, cheapest methods available. The diversion effectively reduces the volume and frequency of the CSO's, but it still fails to address the single most significant cause of these overflows: the impermeability of the city's landscape.

Recognizing Water's Potential

Consider this: A single drop of rain has a life span of approximately ten seconds; it is brief, but pregnant with potential. In a healthy ecosystem, a raindrop extends this life span by providing nourishment wherever it lands. It makes many stops in the ecosystem as it feeds, replenishes, shapes, and cleans the natural landscape and the fauna within, before evaporating to begin the process again.

In the built environment, the life span of a single rain drop depends on where that drop lands. Water that lands on impermeable surfaces such as rooftops, sidewalks, or parking lots, tends to lose purity and potential the moment of impact. Rather than a source of life, the water immediately becomes a waste product, a vehicle for transporting the pollutants that blanket paved surfaces. In the blink of an eye, clean and pure rainwater becomes "stormwater," that omnipotent troublemaker for architects and engineers attempting to design watertight, weatherproof buildings.

With the aim of creating a building that will stand the test of time and weather for centuries, building designers have consistently — and unfortunately — considered stormwater a nuisance. Typically, stormwater is considered to be someone else's problem, and something to be dealt with quickly, methodically and with minimal expense.

Yet the Tanner Creek experience begs the question: if we can't work against water, then why not work with it? One thing remains certain: it continues to rain, and water, staunchly consistent in its physical properties, continues to flow over the surfaces of our urban landscapes. Raindrops landing in the city need not be a waste product, this has only been the status quo. Change begins with each individual building design. A project team can either perpetuate the cycle of impermeable surfaces and rapid discharge, or it can recognize that every drop of water that lands on a site presents an opportunity.

Contaminated stormwater flows into Portland's many storm drains, overburdening the sewer system during many heavy storms.

The Natural Capital Center's Approach

Managing Stormwater

Well aware of the Tanner Creek history and Portland's long and arduous relationship with stormwater, the Natural Capital Center building team made several attempts to work with, rather than against, water. It was logical for Ecotrust to prioritize stormwater as a concern, not only because of the environmental benefits, but because our programmatic approach to every project comes from a bioregional perspective. Given the climate and temperament of the Pacific Northwest, stormwater is a regional issue. Secondly, since most of Ecotrust's work is somehow connected to the health of wild Pacific salmon, it was of primary importance to help enhance the health of the Willamette River, which is home to runs of Chinook salmon and steelhead, listed as threatened under the Endangered Species Act. The architects, engineers, and landscape architects worked with us to create a site design that would effectively contain the building's stormwater on site, where it could irrigate plants and infiltrate at its own pace rather than rushing it to sewer pipes.

When overburdened with stormwater, raw sewage often overflows from the sewer system directly into the Willamette River. This is called a combined-sewer overflow, or CSO.

The bioswales in the Natural Capital Center parking lot are planted with native rushes, sedges, shrubs, and trees.

Our goal was to successfully divert 100% of the site's stormwater from the city's sewer system. To achieve this, the building team devised a series of integrated strategies that ultimately direct almost all stormwater from the Natural Capital Center to infiltration areas incorporated into the parking lot landscape design (see illustration at right). To begin with, a 6,000 square foot green roof blankets the exposed second-story roof. The roof functions like a sponge, using its two inches of soil and top layer of native vegetation to capture and slow the rainwater as it flows from the rooftop to the ground. When saturated, the green roof weighs approximately fourteen pounds per square foot, equal in weight to a conventional gravel roof, enabling the design team to avoid any additional structural, load-bearing, upgrades to the historic building's shell. (See **Anatomy of an Ecoroof** on page 80.)

All of the excess water from the roof is directed into the landscaping on the ground level via a simple network of gutters and downspouts located on the western side of the building. Gravity is the guide at every point in the water's course. The landscaping, engineered and designed as swales planted with native species, receives the building's stormwater from the downspouts and allows the water to seep naturally through the layers of soil into the groundwater below. The irrigation for the landscaping is a removable drip-system that will be taken out once the native plants have become fully established and acclimated. The use of native plants, which are accustomed to the climatic patterns of the region, greatly reduces the amount of irrigation necessary to keep the plants alive.

Two additional swales located on the western edge of the lot receive all of the stormwater that lands in the parking lot, which is gradually sloped in the direction of the swales. Notches cut into the curb along the western side of the lot enable the water to flow directly into the swales. While there are overflow outlets included in each of the four swales, there has yet to be a storm event large enough to send any water into the drains, which are connected to the city's system.[4]

Additional stormwater measures include the use of pavers and permeable asphalt in the parking lot. The original design for the parking lot called for pavers to cover the entire vehicle area. The idea behind pavers is similar to that of permeable asphalt: water seeps through the cracks between the small, square concrete bricks, and percolates naturally through the permeable sublayers and eventually into the natural groundwater below. As a permeable surface, a parking lot can then effectively mimic the infiltration properties of a natural ecosystem.[5] Pavers, however, are still quite expensive, and so, hoping to find a less-expensive though equally effective alternative, the building team selected permeable asphalt.

The use of permeable asphalt as a stormwater management technique is a relatively new idea. In Oregon the Department of Transportation uses permeable asphalt, known as Grade F material, on the top few inches of state highways. There, the larger air spaces prevent water from puddling on the surface; water instead seeps through the top layer to impermeable sublayers a few inches down that send the water off to the sides of the road.

On stretches of highway that are long and straight, where vehicles are traveling quickly with few sharp turns, permeable asphalt is extremely simple to install and effective in performance. In a small parking lot such as that at the Natural Capital Center, it is a different story. Crews struggled to install the asphalt in such a small space, where the rollers were forced to maneuver tight turns at a slow and sloppy pace. Once installed, vehicles moving slowly, stopping, and then turning their wheels into narrow parking spaces, tend to loosen the asphalt at an accelerated rate. The paved parking lot is fast becoming a patchwork of pavers and gravel, and although the permeability of the site remains, it is a little messy. Thus it has been our experience that permeable asphalt is in theory an excellent solution for retaining stormwater on a building site but that in practice, there is still work to be done on product development at the small scale of a parking lot.

Despite this mishap, the common theme throughout the integrated stormwater design was to create a site that would function as though it were 100% permeable even if some sections of the site are in fact impermeable. Paved areas become the critical channels over which water must flow to reach the infiltration areas. There water receives the time and space necessary to seep through layers of substrate and naturally replenish the groundwater. With this integrated design, the Natural Capital Center site has effectively diverted at least 95% of its stormwater from the city's system.[6]

STORMWATER FLOW AT THE NATURAL CAPITAL CENTER

ECOROOF
Evapotranspiration
DOWNSPOUT
Runoff
NW 10TH AVENUE
BIOSWALE
PARKING LOT
BIOSWALE
Permeable asphalt
Evapotranspiration
Evapotranspiration
Runoff
Runoff
Site water retention
Filtration
STORM SEWER
Infiltration

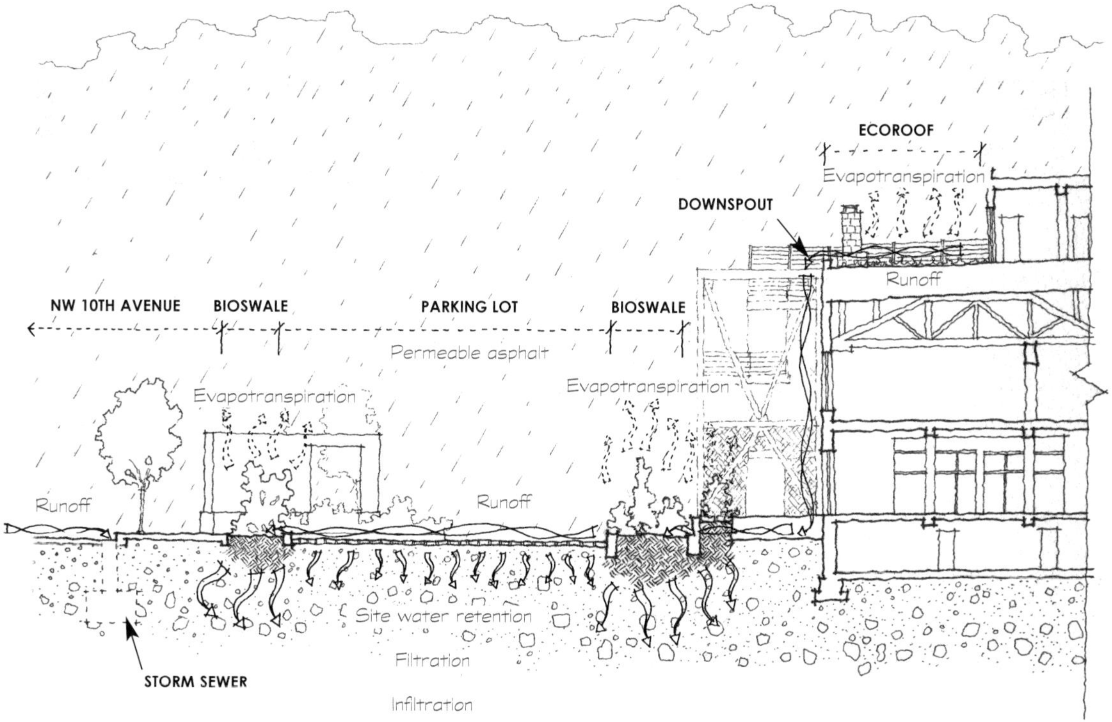

VII

THE ANATOMY OF AN ECOROOF

Ecotrust investigated several green roof systems before selecting the German Famos design. At the time the Famos system was the most lightweight on the market. The two-membrane system is a simple approach that addresses three major concerns of a green roof: water retention, root resistance, and drainage. The system consists of two layers of modified bitumen; the bottom provides waterproofing for the roof, while the top layer of bitumen, inlaid with a thin copper film, provides root resistance and drainage. The copper prevents any roots from penetrating through to the bottom layer — an important component considering that tenacious plant roots can easily grow through conventional membranes, leading to leakage, mold, and mildew.

Attached to the top of the upper roofing membrane is white, unwoven polyester, which holds pockets of hydrogel crystals. These crystals are also found in diapers and landscaping, and create a sort of topography on the roof. They swell up to several times their original size when wet, and act as water-storing units for the plant roots during times when the weather might otherwise be dry. The crystals are installed in long rows. When it rains, their swelling forms peaks in the membrane. The narrow strips in between these peaks become valleys, or drainage outlets for any additional moisture that may build up during a storm.

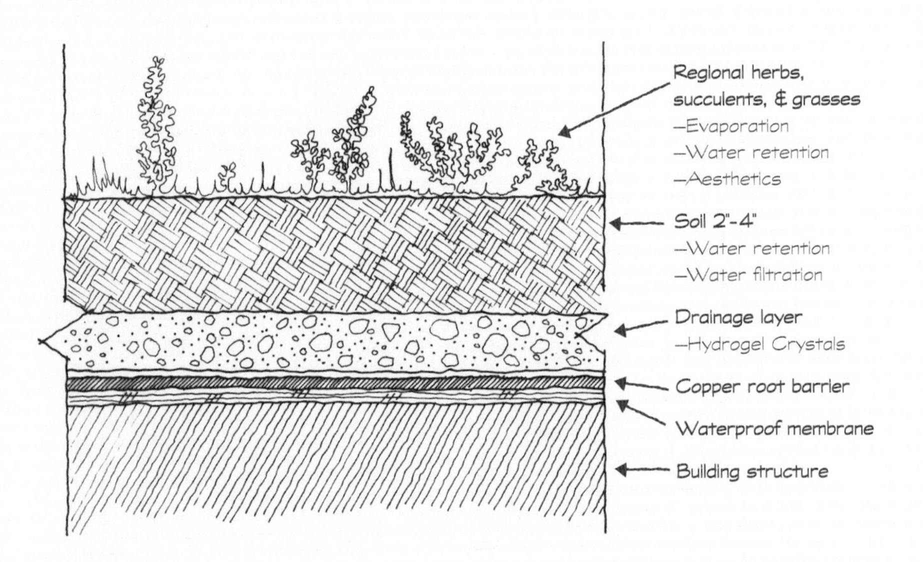

The customized soil was mixed with consideration for weight and absorbency: 30% sandy loam, 15% compost, 40% coarse perlite and pumice, and 15% coconut coir. The compost and sandy loam provide nutrients and slow drainage for the plants, the perlite and pumice aerate the soil and are extremely lightweight, while the coconut coir is highly absorptive, retaining moisture to a capacity several times its size. The soil goes directly over the top layer of bitumen.

Ecotrust explored planting possibilities for the roof from a bioregional perspective, asking such questions as: Which native plants would thrive on an ecoroof? How can we anticipate and plan for natural succession? In addressing stormwater issues, can we also create an ecosystem that is specific to an ecoroof?

To explore such questions, Ecotrust created the following list of selection criteria to determine the appropriate plants:

Native species: Is the plant native to the Pacific Northwest?

Root system: Can the roots support the plant in a 2"–4" substrate?

Drought tolerance: Will the plant survive with little to no irrigation (excluding precipitation)?

Resistance to exposure: Can the plant endure such harsh conditions as full sun and heat, strong winds, and smog?

Availability: Are seeds/plugs/sprigs for this plant readily available?

Maintenance: How much maintenance will this plant require?

Benefits: Do the flowers on this plant attract bees, hummingbirds, butterflies, etc?

Aesthetics: How do the plant's flowers, foliage, and overall composition look? Does this plant work well with the other chosen species?

The following plants were installed on the Natural Capital Center ecoroof as either broadcast seeds, cuttings, or from 3" pots:

Grasses:

- *Danthonia californica* (California oatgrass)
- *Festuca occidentalis* (Western fescue)
- *Festuca rubra v. littoralis* (coastal red fescue)
- *Poa macrantha* (Seashore bluegrass)
- *Carex brevicaulis* (short-stemmed sedge)
- *Koeleria macrantha* (prairie junegrass)
- *Festuca roemeri* (Roemer's fescue)

Herbaceous:

- *Fragaria chiloensis* (coastal strawberry)
- *Fragaria virginiana* (wild strawberry)
- *Heuchera micrantha* (small-flowered alumroot)
- *Achillea millefolium* (yarrow)
- *Anaphalis margaritacea* (pearly everlasting)
- *Eriophyllum lanatum* (Oregon sunshine)
- *Cerastium arvense* (field chickweed)
- *Clarkia amoena* (farewell-to-spring)
- *Gilia capitata* (bluefield gilia)

Sedums (stonecrop):

- *S. oreganum*
- *S. spathulifolium*
- *S. sexangulare**
- *S. oryzifolium 'tinyform'**
- *S. montanum**
- *S. album**
- *S. hybridum**
- *S. dasyphyllum**

*Non-native species; native species not commercially available.

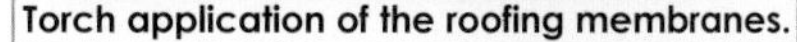
Torch application of the roofing membranes.

The upper membrane, with hydrogel crystals underneath white polyester fabric.

Hydro-mulching over the broadcast seeds and sedum sprigs.

Sedum in bloom in the ecoroof's second year.

RECONNECTING PEOPLE AND WATER

Urban Water Works (UWW) is a Portland-based non-profit whose mission and actions manifest many of the working principles needed to establish healthy water systems. Since its founding in 1999 this organization, fueled entirely by the devotion of a core group of volunteers, has worked tirelessly to create a network of water projects throughout the city of Portland that collectively make the city's water systems and watershed fully visible and integrated into the daily lives of Portland residents. Integral to their work is collaboration between the arts and sciences. For each project UWW brings together landscape designers, engineers, artists, urban planners, hydrologists, teachers, wetland ecologists, students, and community members who brainstorm functional and imaginative solutions for stormwater management, wastewater treatment, or general beautification of a building site or plot of vacant land. Examples of their work include schoolyard restoration projects such as the DaVinci Living Water Garden at the DaVinci Arts Middle School in northeast Portland. Here UWW worked with students and teachers to transform an old tennis court into a garden that cleans over 200,000 gallons per year of stormwater runoff from the school's roof and parking lot.

The Living Water Garden at the DaVinci Arts Middle School in northeast Portland.

Other programs include the Ridgetop to Rivers project, an investigation into the history of local watersheds that includes developing community-based plans for stormwater management and watershed improvement; a Speakers Series that has included presentations by Herbert Dreiseitl of Atelier Dreiseitl and Betsy Damon of Keepers of the Water; and, most recently, the establishment of Ecoroofs Everywhere, an independent program that promotes the widespread use of green roofs as a building strategy that benefits local watersheds. ■

Conserving Water

The abundance of rain in the Pacific Northwest often misleads both visitors and residents into believing that water conservation is something left for desert activists of the great Southwest. This is far from true. Water distribution in this rainy region is seasonal, meaning that despite the soggy months of winter and spring, the summers are dry, and the temperate areas still go through periods of intense drought. Water conservation is therefore essential to the design of a building in the Northwest; it helps avoid a false sense of abundance and instead ensures that the resource will be available in periods of scarcity.

The water conservation measures in the Natural Capital Center are varied and less conspicuous than the stormwater components. All of the faucets and showerheads (located in the basement locker rooms) have flow fixtures that reduce the flow to 0.5 gallons per minute (gpm) and 2.0 gpm, respectively. The toilets are low-flush models that require a maximum of 1.6 gallons per flush while the urinals use one gallon of water or less per flush.

Ecotrust attempted unsuccessfully to locate dual-flush toilets. The idea behind their design is quite simple: they offer two options for flushing, one for low-volume flushes and one for higher-volume flushes, depending on the need. The product was first introduced in Australia, where water-conservation efforts have been far more demanding and prominent for decades, and they are also common in parts of Europe.

We also attempted to incorporate waterless urinals into the building, but found that they were not permitted by the plumbing code that was in effect during construction. A conventional urinal uses at least one gallon of water with every flush. One study, conducted by an architecture firm in Seattle, Washington, found that 75 men were flushing 50,000 gallons of water per year down conventional urinals. By comparison, waterless urinals can completely erase such levels of water consumption from a building's footprint.

The Oregon Plumbing Board is monitoring a trial use of the urinals in a state park along the coast, claiming that the product has not yet been proven effective or sanitary. The technology behind waterless urinals has in fact been around for over 100 years, and was first developed in Switzerland. Physically, the product looks just like a conventional urinal, but instead of running water it uses a liquid that is lighter than urine and sits in the urinal's trap. Following the course of gravity, urine passes through the liquid and into the plumbing system; the liquid also prevents sewer gases from rising into the bathroom. When maintained correctly, the waterless urinals are an excellent option for water conservation.

Composting toilets also use no or very little water and produce a valuable fertilizer. Like flushless urinals, they produce significant water savings. However, the maintenance requirements, although minor, limit their rapid adoption. In addition, they are generally not cost competitive where a central waste water system already exists. While used primarily in rural or remote areas, the use of composting toilets is slowly increasing in urban and commercial applications, and their widespread use could significantly reduce water use, enhance water quality, and reduce sewage treatment costs.

Some of our strongest efforts went into exploring the option of installing cisterns in the basement to store rainwater for non-potable uses around the building such as irrigation, flushing, and the fire sprinkler system, but we ran into challenges with the Water Bureau. Had we decided to use stored ranwater for interior uses, the building would have required a dual plumbing system, one that, according to the Water Bureau, could potentially contaminate the treated, potable water from the city's supply with non-potable water from the cisterns. The city's concerns eventually overruled our desire to challenge this status quo. We finally backed down and moved on, taking comfort in the idea that the building's relatively flexible design could allow for changes to the water components in the future.

Moving Forward — Variations in Scale

Zooming out to the bigger picture, what if, within the scope of the entire building community, water was considered a technical and creative resource rather than a nuisance? Since it is always present, what if, as a rule, architects and engineers treated water as an ally, even as a building material, something akin to bricks, wood, or steel? What if, in a similar vein, the building was treated as an ecosystem, one in which the natural processes of water, such as multiple-use and infiltration, were kept intact rather than disrupted? What if water's functional value was complemented by its value as a creative medium — an element that triggers all of our senses and inspires and educates the community? Finally, what if buildings were located, even moved if necessary, to work with water's natural drainage patterns, rather than moving water to accommodate buildings?

These questions are not far-fetched. Some of them made their way into the design of the Natural Capital Center. They are also ideas that are being considered and put to use at even larger scales by city governments, non-profits, and design teams in many places around the world, including Portland, Seattle, and

Stormwater Filtration: A Technical Solution

Infiltration with bioswales and permeable paving is the ideal stormwater management strategy for many, though not all, building sites. For existing properties that have contaminated soils, or where incorporating swales, landscaping, or more permeable paving is simply not possible, another option is to install a stormwater filter, such as the design pictured below, developed by Stormwater Management, Inc. Based in Portland, Stormwater Management, Inc. offers a range of filtration systems that can be installed in parking lots, manholes, and locations where they can effectively remove high levels of pollutants such as sediments, oil and grease, soluble heavy metals, organics, and soluble nutrients. Their filters can be customized for a site's specific needs, and have been widely recognized as a best management practice for stormwater management. For more information, visit their web site at www.stormwaterinc.com.

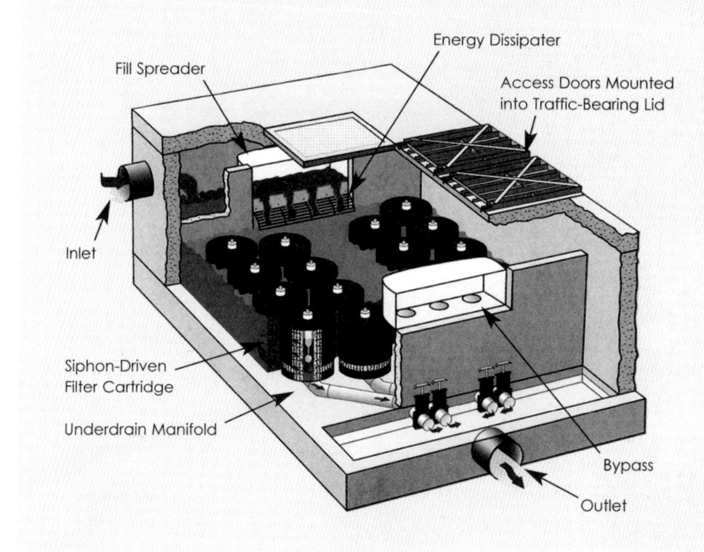

Water Staircase and Market Square Design, City of Hattersheim, Germany. Designed by Atelier Dreiseitl, 1988–1993, using recycled rainwater throughout the extensive design.

Vancouver, British Columbia; Northern California, Los Angeles, Chicago, Toronto, China, and Western Europe.

City Block

Consider the work of Herbert Dreiseitl. His studio, Atelier Dreiseitl, emerged in Germany in the early 1980's, when Dreiseitl and his peers began to think seriously about water in the built environment and to search for ways to make stormwater, infiltration, and water consumption visible processes to the public eye. The fundamental design principles governing the work of his studio, which consists of architects, landscape architects, engineers, and artists, are to observe, build, and experiment with water in order to understand its ecology and essence. Dreiseitl's work reflects the belief that the built environment should celebrate water's aesthetic quality, versatility, and interconnectedness with all aspects of nature and culture, while educating the public about water's functional roles in an urban setting. His studio is extremely active, working on designs throughout Europe and North America.

Recognizing the studio's unique creativity, the City of Portland has hosted multiple conferences and design charettes at which representatives from Atelier Dreiseitl were featured guests. Particularly relevant to Portland's situation is Dreiseitl's view that stormwater management is not only a necessary infrastructure, it is an opportunity to increase city residents' awareness of water's functions. Because of water's innate ability to activate all senses with its creation of light, sound, and atmosphere, the water processes in Dreiseitl's designs are made visible both for education and inspiration.

Dreiseitl returned to Portland in 2003 to work with the city to design a park in the River District. The park is the second in a series of three that are included in the master plan for northwest Portland's River District.[7] Historically this section of the city has been disconnected from the banks of the nearby Willamette River by a large swath of industrial land and rail yards. The redevelopment of these neighborhoods is placing great emphasis on reconnecting the city to the river through a series of parks that include water features, wetlands, and a boardwalk that spans several city blocks and ends at the riverbank, near the historic location of the mouth of Tanner Creek.

While Dreiseitl's designs for the River District park are still in the early stages, they will almost certainly include many principles from his other projects, such as transforming a single city block into a creative, interactive display of water's processes; making visible and audible water's different patterns of flow, reactions to light, and relationships with gravity and topography, and involving local citizens, artists, and public agencies in necessary and active dialogue about the value of water in the urban landscape.

Neighborhood

Working with stormwater on a scale larger than a single city block can present greater challenges but also more opportunities for integration and synergy, as illustrated by Patrick Condon's work at the University of British Columbia. Condon and his team of designers, many of whom are graduate students in the university's Landscape Architecture program, propose that designers and public agencies consider stormwater management on a neighborhood, watershed, and regional scale. Such a perspective takes a wider view of a neighborhood in order to evaluate the entire site's natural drainage patterns by observing where stormwater would flow if uninterrupted by paved areas, curbs, and drains. The design of the neighborhood maximizes these natural drainage patterns and works with them, rather than disrupting and diverting the water's course. Such designs include green spaces that are meant to be used for recreation, natural habitat, and infiltration areas for stormwater management. The sites function as if they had no impermeable surfaces. This means that they maximize all permeable areas, and where this is not possible, use impermeable surfaces (roads, for example) as conduits that direct water to the nearest permeable areas (swales on the sides of roads).

On this larger scale, once given the freedom to flow freely and infiltrate at its own pace, water becomes the connection between the natural and built environments in a way that is visible to residents of the neighborhood. Individual buildings in the neighborhood are designed to retain as much of their stormwater on site as possible through green roofs, cisterns, and landscaping that includes infiltration areas. Any excess water flows into a larger common infiltration area, whose location is determined by where the water would settle on its own, given the natural topography of the neighborhood. Making the entire process visible gives residents and visitors a heightened awareness not only of water's physical function but also of its potential as an endless source of life rather than decay.

Watershed

Condon's large-scale work is especially effective for newer developments, those that begin with a plot of land, an abundance of room, and an entire landscape as the blank canvas. But what can be recommended to the thousands of established

CONDON'S EAST CLAYTON NEIGHBORHOOD DESIGN

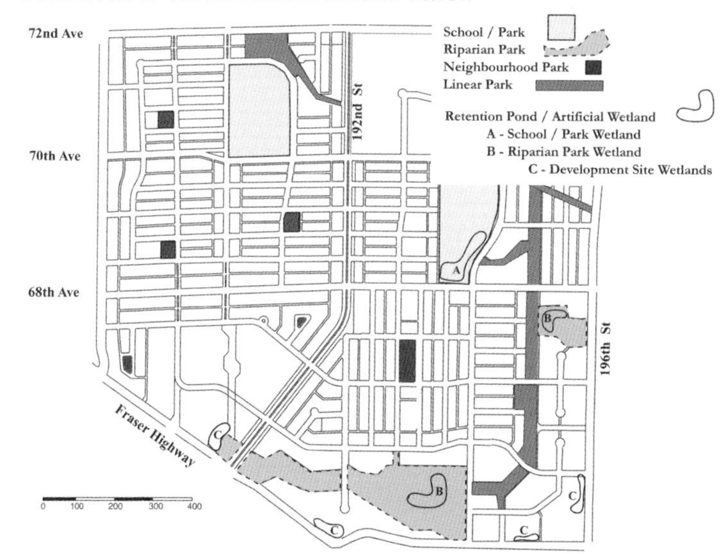

Overview of the Neighborhood Concept Plan for East Clayton (Surrey, British Columbia) with extensive park systems, retention ponds, and artificial wetlands for stormwater treatment.

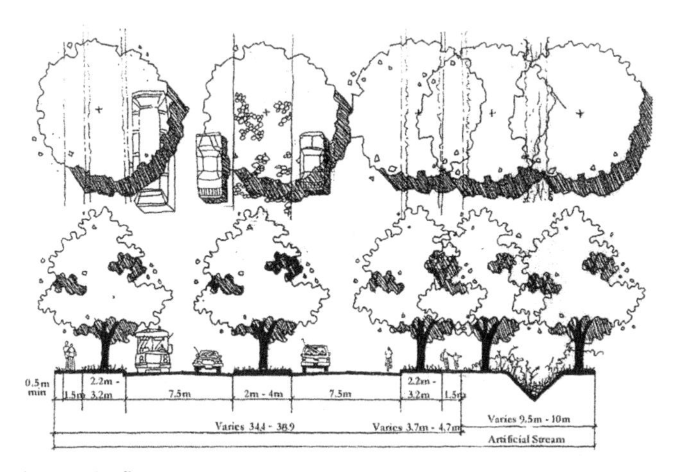

Stormwater flows over roads without curbs, artificial streams along roadside catch the water and send it to retention areas. Emphasis on narrow roads with large trees for shade,buffering, and absorption.

communities that have experienced the full course of stormwater mismanagement and now grapple with seemingly irreversible problems? While many towns may be able to integrate various aspects of designs like Condon's or Atelier Dreiseitl's, the town of Napa, in Northern California, has yet another suggestion.

The sleepy town sits in the middle of a valley of the same name, through which flows the mighty Napa River. For years Napa has been the central hub for the grape-growing industry of Northern California. In recent times, however, it has fallen into an economic slump. Over the years the forces of agriculture and other economic development have blocked, diverted, leveed, and polluted the Napa River, so much that the river has begun to fight back with floods after every major rainstorm, consistently causing devastating damage to local property. In the early 1990s the Army Corps of Engineers proposed a solution: submerge the feisty river into a deep concrete channel that would flow in a straight line through the middle of the city. Its aesthetic: concrete and rip rap. Its funding: at least half of the cost would be borne by local residents.

With the leadership of a few extremely committed local citizens, the town came up with an alternative solution: treat the river as an ally rather than an enemy; work with it rather than against it. Community members proposed returning the river to its natural course. They were even willing to move existing homes, businesses, and railroad tracks built in the original floodplain and to prevent any future development in the floodplain. They suggested that the Corps remove levees and take down or rebuild bridges that were too low. Essentially, the community proposed that the town listen to the river and simply let it be. The reward: over 650 acres of created or restored wetlands in and around the downtown, a boost to an economy that would benefit from increased recreation and tourists, and, finally, peace with the river.

After years of finagling with the Corps and conducting a series of campaigns to convince the entire town of the project's value, Napa's "living river" approach to long-term stormwater problems has become an unprecedented success and inspiration to communities enduring similar struggles. It has been no small task. The project called for undying commitment and long-term vision from community members, a broad perspective on development within a watershed, and collaboration with a federal agency whose history of stormwater management has not always been favorable to natural systems. Yet the rewards that came from making peace with the Napa River have far outweighed the difficulties. They remind us that collaboration and integration need not be limited in scale.[8]

Restoration activities on the Napa River include removal of contaminated soil and retaining walls so that the river can be reconnected to its floodplain, providing natural storage for flood waters and enhancing salmon habitat.

Conclusion

Single building, city block, neighborhood, watershed — regardless of scale the themes remain the same. Water's behavior is inevitable: It is stubborn, and when treated as an obstacle, as Tanner Creek or the Napa River remind us, it will fight back. When considered an ally, water's potential for function, inspiration, and education is endless. Over the years the built environment has generally lost contact with this idea, but examples of successful water planning around the world indicate that things are beginning to change. In Portland, efforts by the City, nonprofit organizations, and individual developers show that building projects are beginning to work in favor of the local watershed. The Natural Capital Center attempted a regional solution to a regional problem: keeping stormwater on site, recognizing water for its creative, rather than debilitating qualities, and using water as a link between a building and its inhabitants, its site, its neighbors, the city, and the living watershed. ■

MATERIALS

by Bettina von Hagen

More than any other set of decisions, apart from the always important selection of location, the choice of materials defines a building — how it looks, feels, and performs; how long it lives and how adaptable it is to new uses; whether the products it yields at deconstruction form new buildings or add to the nation's hazardous waste inventory. Materials choices are, of course, inextricably linked with design choices. The choice of structural system, whether steel, concrete, wood, brick, or adobe, strongly influences the design, and design decisions in turn determine the potential materials. Materials choices also contribute to the amount of energy buildings consume. While most energy use goes to heating and cooling a building, a large proportion is embodied, or contained, in the building materials — in their extraction, manufacturing, distribution, installation, maintenance, and disposal.

Builders generally select materials on the basis of performance, price, availability, and appearance. However, there are other important dimensions to consider. The building products industry contributes significantly to the domestic economy. Over 3,000 manufacturers supply the $800 billion commercial and residential construction markets with more than three million products.[1] Unfortunately, the industry also contributes in less positive ways, through its energy use, solid and hazardous waste generation, air pollution, water use and contamination.

The impacts of material extraction, manufacturing, transportation, and installation are often called "externalities" because they are not internalized (i.e. included) in the cost of the product. Instead, these costs are borne by the land, earth, and water, and by the health of people, including the ultimate tenants of the building. The U.S Environmental Protection Agency (EPA) estimates that indoor pollution alone — caused by materials such as particleboard, paints, adhesives, carpets, and plastics — is responsible for more than 11,000 deaths per year from cancer and kidney and respiratory disease.[2]

Selecting materials for green building involves explicitly considering the full life cycle of a building material, including its intended and unintended effects. This greatly increases the complexity and number of decisions to make when selecting materials, and involves making trade-offs among product attributes. The Natural Capital Center building team attempted to navigate these uncharted and changing waters using Ecotrust's values and mission as a guide. Fortunately, there is now a systematic

Metafore's third floor office showcases a variety of domestic and tropical woods certified by the Forest Stewardship Council.

attempt to evaluate this complex information through life-cycle analysis and life-cycle thinking — a new generation of more powerful decision tools described in detail later in this chapter.

Selecting Materials for the Natural Capital Center

A building project requires a huge number of decisions that need to be made quickly ("Make up your mind or we will lose thousands in construction delays!"). Without complete product information or a method to measure relative costs and benefits, some simple decision rules need to be developed. Ecotrust's decision rules — choosing locally made materials, rewarding good forest management, and supporting new markets and products — reflected our regional context and our efforts to support local entrepreneurs and to conserve healthy, intact, functioning ecosystems. Whether a decision rule prioritizes high recycled content or low toxicity, the important thing is to develop a simple system that guides product choices and can be communicated effectively to the design and construction team to facilitate rapid and consistent decision-making.

The Natural Capital Center building team was aided by the fact that we had fewer decisions to make than is the case with new construction. Many of our materials choices had been made a century ago when the building was erected. Nevertheless, we were still left with hundreds of product decisions to make and thousands of trade-offs to consider.

The building itself begged for reduction, frugality, and simplicity. The old Douglas-fir plank flooring, the massive posts, beams, and trusses, and the warm brick set a high standard for any additional materials, and mostly discouraged additions or embellishments. We were guided by the maxim "less is more" and added paint, walls, and wall coverings only where required. Our desire to maximize natural light penetration into the building and to maintain openness and views also contributed to an open design that significantly reduced the use of materials. We fought every impulse and need to create floor-to-ceiling walls and enclosures, and did so only when the fire code, security concerns, or use mandated them.

Iisaak Forest Enterprises on Vancouver Island uses small patch cuts and helicopter logging to harvest wood. The cedar paneling in the conference center (inset) was supplied by Iisaak.

Material use (and labor) was also reduced by our "low-finish" aesthetic, which included leaving pipes, wires, and mechanical equipment exposed. It also meant giving the posts, beams, and trusses only a minimal cleaning and declaring the remaining paint, spots and nicks to be part of the building's history. We carefully removed thick layers of paint from the three primary exterior façades, restored the original brick and stucco, but left the fourth "secondary" wall unpainted, preserving the names of towns that had guided the activities of the old warehouse and distribution business that had occupied the building for decades.

Reuse was also an obvious strategy. The interior demolition and the deconstruction of an adjacent building, described in Chapter 5, yielded a wealth of materials, primarily stone, wood, diamond plate, and old gears and pipes. We rented a surface yard and stored all the materials we could imagine using and sold the rest. We also hired a crew to carefully demolish the interior honeycombs of offices that had developed over the decades, yielding tongue-and-groove paneling, doors, and hardware that we added to our "boneyard" of useful materials. This boneyard then became the first source of materials for both the primary redevelopment and the ensuing tenant improvements. The posts and beams that had supported the adjacent building were incorporated into the building of the third floor addition. Additional beams were remilled to produce internal doors, trim, and furniture.

The tongue-and-groove paneling, which unfortunately was painted on one side with lead paint, was reversed to serve as new paneling or as half walls to separate offices. The diamond plate which had protected the Douglas-fir plank flooring from heavy carts and forklifts used to transport material now serves as a wall covering in the conference room. We used the old granite curbstones to produce benches that provide seating for people waiting for the streetcar. The old gears and pulleys that transported material between the floors of the building found new life as bases for tables. While incorporating these materials into new products sometimes took more time, energy, and expense than their new functional equivalents, they contributed considerably to the aesthetics and sense of history of the redeveloped building.

New materials choices were much more difficult. Price, performance, and aesthetic considerations narrowed the field, but still left plenty of products to consider on the basis of recycled content, ease of recycling, responsible use of natural resources, low toxicity, indoor air quality, and a myriad of other dimensions. We also considered the "story" potential of a product: to what extent did the product tell a compelling story about a critical environmental problem or solution? Wherever possible, we also wanted to serve as catalysts in enhancing markets or in promoting important emerging products.

SAMPLE LIFE-CYCLE ANALYSIS

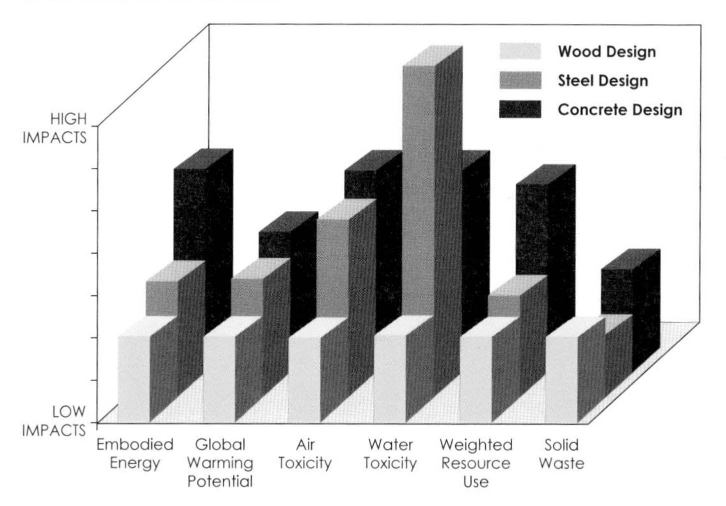

Wood is a better choice than steel or concrete based on a comparative life-cycle analysis of environmental impacts.

Source: Adapted with permission from Robert Kozak and Christopher Gaston, "Life-Cycle Analysis," presented at the Workshop on Climate Change and Forestry, Orcas Island, WA, November 13–16, 2001.

Cradle-to-cradle is a profoundly different way to think about a product's life cycle and replaces the **cradle-to-grave** perspective, in which a material progresses from extraction to disposal in a linear process. Cradle-to-cradle is a closed loop with significant implications for product design and manufacturing — the application of cradle-to-cradle principles creates cyclical material flows that eliminate the concept of waste and emulate the earth's nutrient cycles. Each material in a product is designed to be safe and effective, and to provide high quality resources for subsequent generations of products. All materials are conceived as nutrients, circulating safely and productively in either natural or industrial cycles.

Extended producer responsibility (EPR) entails making manufacturers responsible for the entire lifecycle of the products and packaging they produce. One aim of EPR policies is to incorporate the environmental costs of products into their price. Another is to shift the economic burden of managing products that have reached the end of their useful life from local government and taxpayers to their consumers and producers, who are in the best position to reuse or redesign the product materials. EPR initiatives include product take-back programs, deposit refund systems, product fees and taxes, and minimum recycled-content laws.

Product take-back is a promising policy tool for implementing the principle of Extended Producer Responsibility. Take-back initiatives place the responsibility of product disposal on the product manufacturer, and create incentives for designers to develop products that are reusable, made of recycled materials, and are recyclable.

This design of products for end-of-life is called **design for recycling** or **design for disassembly**. This approach to product design focuses on materials and assembly methods which allow the product and its parts to be easily reused, re-manufactured, or recycled at the end of life. ■

A PRODUCT'S LIFE CYCLE — FROM CRADLE TO CRADLE

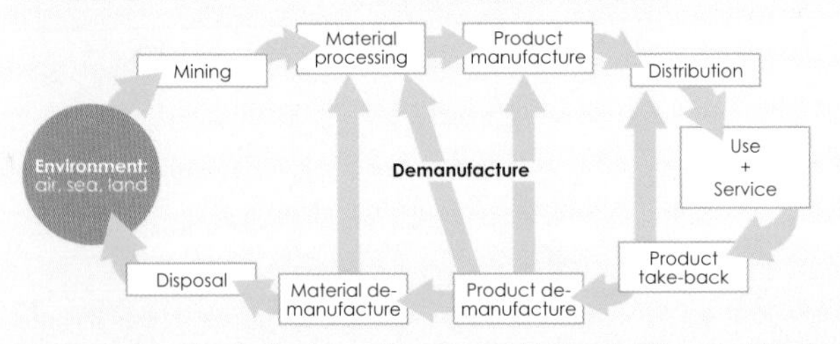

Source: Systems Realization Laboratory, George W. Woodruff School of Mechanical Engineering, Georgia Institute of Technology, Atlanta, Georgia.

The international non-profit Forest Stewardship Council (**FSC**) independently certifies wood products, evaluating whether they come from forests that are well-managed from an environmental, social, and ecological perspective.

Making trade-offs among these considerations was sometimes extremely difficult. For the outside deck, was it better to use **FSC** certified ipe, a hardwood from the Amazon basin, or the more local "plastic lumber" which provides an important market for plastic recycling? For the paint, was it better to choose low-VOC (volatile organic compounds) paint or locally produced post-consumer higher VOC recycled paint? Should the bathroom stalls be made of plastic with 25% recycled content or lower-priced metal that is easier to recycle? Should the cabinets be made of strawboard which uses waste material or virgin wood that is FSC certified? Is it better to select an adhesive which compromises indoor air quality or one that is highly toxic during the manufacturing process? In assessing whether the original wood windows should be replaced with new energy efficient windows, how should we balance the generation of waste, use of new materials, and loss of the building's history with gains in energy efficiency?

The Emerging Art of Life-Cycle Analysis

The emerging life-cycle assessment tools that measure a product's "cradle-to-grave" or "cradle-to-cradle" impact — from extraction to manufacturing, use, and disposal or re-use — are designed to evaluate these types of trade-offs. Life-cycle analysis (LCA) is simple in concept but often highly complex in execution. Conceptually, life-cycle analysis considers all the impacts of a product from its extraction or harvesting of raw material, through its refining or manufacturing, to its transport, installation, and maintenance, and its eventual disposal or reuse. In some cases, the calculations can be fairly straight-forward. The complexity increases when products are made from various raw materials or components, each with their own life history, or when the raw materials come from a variety of sources which change in response to price or availability. Life-cycle analysis is also very place-specific: transportation costs and other factors will vary significantly based on where the product is used. For example, the choice of steel in Winnipeg, Canada uses considerably more transportation energy than in Toronto, where many of the steel producers are located. It is also difficult to know where to stop the analysis: should the cost of energy, for example, include the global costs of oil spills and contamination, or the health effects of air pollution, or the financial, environmental, and cultural costs of salmon decline attributable to dams and hydroelectric facilities?

The various life-cycle analysis systems under development[3] are guided by a set of global standards developed by the International Standards Organization (ISO). These standards, outlined in the ISO 14040 series,[4] describe a standard process for LCA which includes defining the goals and scope of the study, conducting an inventory analysis (a measurement of the inflows and outflows of materials and energy), impact analysis (assessing the environmental impact of those flows), and drawing interpretations and conclusions. The first large-scale commercial use of LCA in the United States was done by The Coca-Cola Company and assessed the relative merits of glass versus plastic bottles, and led to the virtual abandonment of glass soda bottles. Since then, LCA has been used to address a myriad of questions important to consumers, such as evaluating cloth versus disposable diapers (disposable diapers generally win due to the high air and water pollution generated by growing cotton), paper versus foam cups (foam appears to be the winner, based on using less energy and water to make), and plastic versus paper shopping bags (answer depends on who conducts the study and the assumptions made about how full the bags are).[5]

MATERIALS IN THE NATURAL CAPITAL CENTER

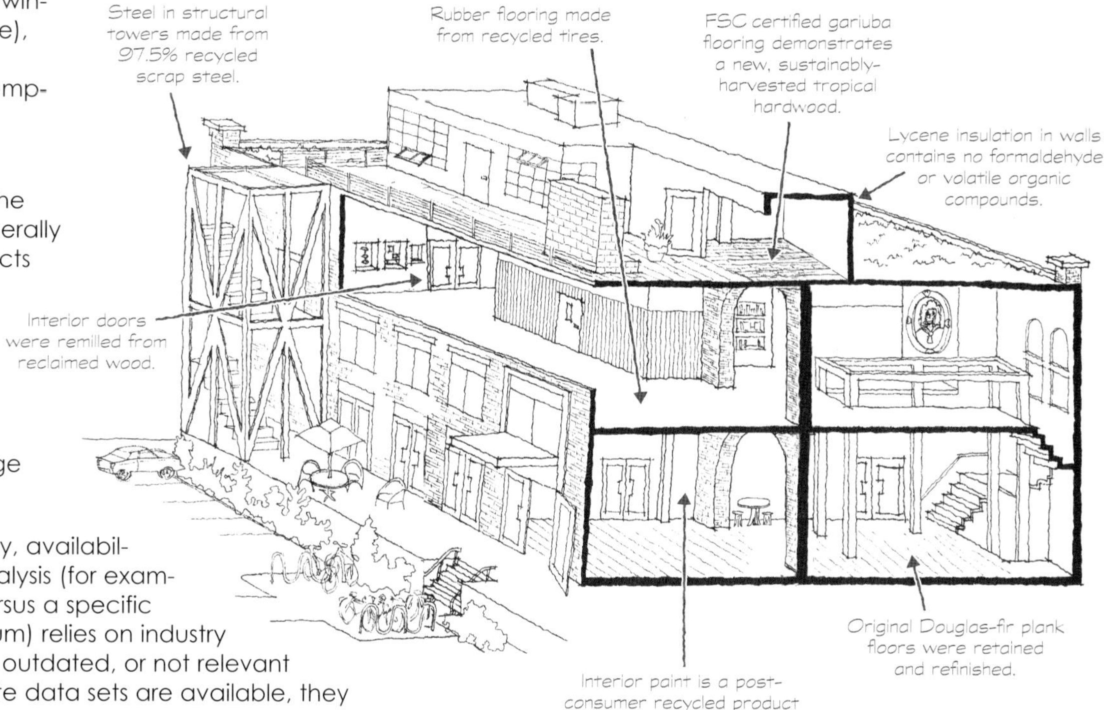

Conducting life-cycle analysis on buildings adds another dimension — estimating the useful life of the product (or of the building). Building materials generally have a long life, and thus the environmental impacts relating to their use — as opposed to their manufacturing or disposal — tend to dominate their overall life-cycle profile. However, while the service life of a building product may be long, the product may be replaced sooner for aesthetic reasons or a change in use — a frequent event in commercial buildings where tenants may change every five to ten years.[6]

Another challenge of life-cycle analyis is the quality, availability, and reliability of the data. Generic product analysis (for example, assessing the life cycle impacts of linoleum versus a specific product in this category such as Forbo's marmoleum) relies on industry averages, which may be inaccurate, inconsistent, outdated, or not relevant to the geography in question.[7] Even when accurate data sets are available, they may be proprietary.

VIII

A SAMPLING OF NATURAL CAPITAL CENTER MATERIALS

▲The most significant way to reduce a building's ecological footprint is through the materials that are not used. The Natural Capital Center's open office plans and shared common areas cut material use for tenant improvements by half or more, while distributing natural light and fresh air more effectively.

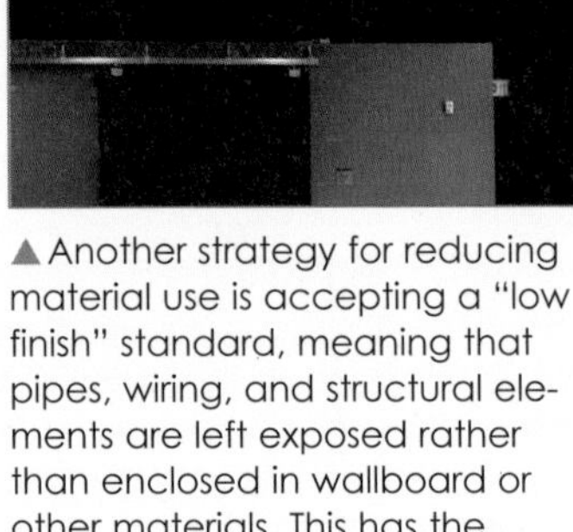

▲Another strategy for reducing material use is accepting a "low finish" standard, meaning that pipes, wiring, and structural elements are left exposed rather than enclosed in wallboard or other materials. This has the added advantage of greatly facilitating repairs and maintenance, saving time and money.

▲The third floor addition was built with posts and beams from the deconstruction of an adjacent building and some limited interior demolition. This reclaimed wood was also used for doors, trim, furniture, railings, and other wood uses, saving money on materials and providing beautiful, tight grain wood.

▲Careful demolition of interior offices and an adjacent building prior to redevelopment yielded an abundance of materials, including these doors which were used to frame the offices of ShoreBank Pacific, Ecotrust's economic development partner. Old, massive fire doors were also used to build a movable wall to separate the north and south rooms of the conference center.

▲Site development unearthed beautiful granite curbstones, which were polished and engraved with words of wisdom from leading thinkers and activists. From curbstones to benches, the granite has new life providing seating and reflection for those waiting for the street car, or pausing to watch a bocce ball tournament in nearby Jamison Park.

Gears from the various freight
›vators formed the base for
s and other tables in the build-
j. Salvaged materials — wood,
re, the old furnace, old nails —
›re used to build directories,
›at racks, tables, benches,
airs, and other useful items.
nile not always the cheapest
ernative, these items add con-
erable character to the build-
j, as well as providing an
›portunity for local fine furniture
akers to display their skills.

▲ All the interior paint comes from a latex paint recycling program developed by Metro, Portland's regional government, which collects leftover paint from households in an attempt to avoid illegal disposal in Portland's landfills and waterways. The paint is remixed, tinted to either standard or special order color requirements, and resold. Although comprised of many paint types, the initial use and remixing releases many of the original volatile organic compounds (VOCs), yielding a paint which is low-VOC, virtually odorless, and easy to apply.

▲ While we were able to retain the original Douglas-fir plank flooring on the first floor, seismic codes required covering the second floor with a plywood diaphragm, thus requiring a new floor covering. We chose rubber tiles made from post-consumer recycled rubber tires. The interlocking rubber tiles require no adhesives, reducing their potential for toxic emissions and facilitating their reconfiguration or removal. In addition, the rubber provides welcome sound absorption and a comfortable walking surface.

▲ Led by tenant Metafore, FSC certified guariuba (*Clarisia racemosa*) flooring was chosen for the third floor lobby to showcase an underutilized but strikingly beautiful and colorful tropical hardwood. While an acre of tropical forest may have hundreds of tree species, only a few are commercially valued leading to destructive "high grading" where cutting is spread over a large area to obtain the few commercial species. Development of markets for species like guariuba contribute to better and more sustainable forest management.

▲ Gregory Acker, a green architect and manager of the City's commercial green building program, designed the Office of Sustainable Development's new office in the Natural Capital Center using donated doors for the office partitions and desks. The doors, made by The Collins Companies of FSC certified particle board surrounding FSC certified cores, were rejected by the original purchaser because of minor flaws and donated to the City by Collins. Acker estimates the reuse of the donated doors saved $40–45,000 over the purchase of new workstations.

SHIFTING RESOURCE EXTRACTION FROM RURAL LANDSCAPES TO URBAN LANDFILLS

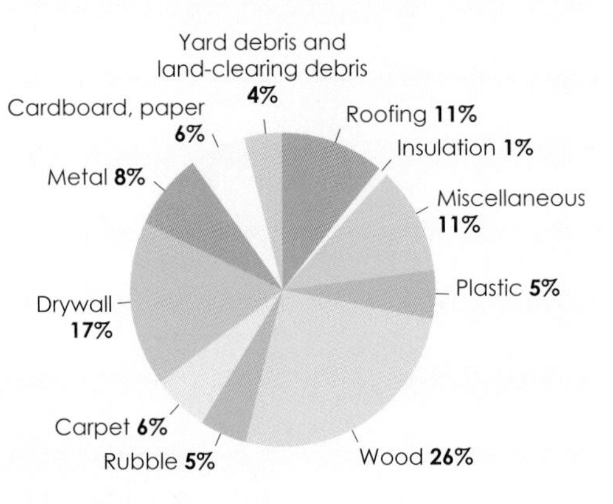

Source: Interpretation of Department of Environmental Quality 1998 Waste Composition Study

Demolition of residential and commercial buildings generates about 65 million tons of construction debris annually, with wood, drywall, yard debris, and cardboard making up over half of the total. Experts estimate that 50-60% of this material could be recycled, reducing pressure on both raw materials and landfills.[8] It also makes good sense for builders. In Portland, for example, garbage disposal fees are $62.50 per ton while construction waste can be dropped off at a recycling facility for fees ranging from nothing to $35 per ton (and in some cases sold at a profit).[9] Recycling, salvaging, reusing, and remanufacturing construction waste can also spawn whole new industries, generating jobs and new business formation, as described in Chapter 2. ■

GENERATION OF DEMOLITION DEBRIS IN THE U.S.

Building Type	Demolitions per Year	Average Building Size sq. ft. (m²)	Average Generation Rate lbs/sq. ft. (kg/m²)	Total tons (tonnes)
Residential	245,000	1,396 (130)	115 (560)	19.7 (20) million
Non-residential	43,795	13,300 (1,235)	155 (755)	45.1 (45.8) million
TOTAL	288,795	—	—	64.8 (65.8) million

Source: Tables 5 and 6, *Characterization of Building-Related Construction and Demolition Debris in the United States*, EPA, 1998.

One manufacturing process can use multiple resources and produce multiple products, raising questions about how these flows should be allocated among these products. For example, crude oil refining yields acetone, gasoline, fuel oil, asphalt, and other products. Should the environmental impacts be allocated on the basis of mass or energy or some other unit? Should it make a difference if the product being evaluated is a primary product or a by-product of the manufacturing process? For example, the Natural Capital Center chose to use sheetrock (also called wallboard and dry wall) made in part from smokestack residues in power plants — this process, known as flue-gas desulfurization, captures suspended gypsum and reduces the need for mining virgin material. In conducting a life-cycle analysis, should the recycled content of the sheetrock be charged with all of the environmental impacts of the raw material extraction and manufacturing, or is the allocation different because it is a by-product and its reuse provides an environmental benefit?

Once the difficult allocation issues are resolved, the job gets even harder — evaluating and assessing the impacts. The impacts are grouped into categories, which generally include global warming, ozone depletion, ecosystem toxicity, effects on human health, habitat depletion, and hazardous and solid waste generation. When the study's goals are first established, the researchers decide which of these categories to include, based on availability and reliability of data, and the research budget and timeline. Unfortunately, the study's design is sometimes based on the conclusion that the LCA's sponsor (often a product manufacturer) would like to reach. Before relying on LCA data, the first thing to check is the sponsor of the study. If it is a product manufacturer or industry association, and the LCA results support the sponsor's product, one should carefully evaluate the scope and methods of the analysis to determine the extent of bias.

Some categories are harder than others. Evaluating a product's contribution to global warming is a relatively well-developed process, although determining the effects of global warming is much more complex. More difficult still is estimating the impact on human health from hazardous and toxic materials, which depends on the likelihood of and sensitivity to exposure, as well as the presence and persistence of the toxins. Perhaps the most difficult task is estimating a product's effect on habitat loss and biodiversity. With the exception of terrestrial vertebrates, we have identified only a small fraction of all the species occurring on Earth, and can only speculate about how a product's extraction, manufacturing, or disposal might affect these species' long-term viability.

The impact assessment phase presents great challenges, but the next step in the analysis is even more problematic: expressing the results of each impact so that they can be compared and then traded off depending on the project's priorities. In addition, this methodology needs to be consistently applied so that one LCA study can be compared to another. While there is considerable activity in this arena, the goal of a consistent, universally adopted materials scorecard is still far off, and reducing these comparisons to a single number may never be achieved.

Life-Cycle Thinking: A Tool to Use with Imperfect Information

While life-cycle analysis clearly has a long way to go, life-cycle thinking can be a very useful tool. *Environmental Building News*, the leading green building newsletter, has developed a useful framework to address the hierarchy of life-cycle stages of most building materials.[10] Since the use phase is most important in durable materials, environmental considerations associated with use and maintenance are considered first, followed by manufacturing, then raw material acquisition and preparation, and finally disposal or reuse. This hierarchy also has the advantage of requiring information that is most available to the building team: product use and manufacturing. Assembling impacts in this way can greatly simplify the assessment process. For example, the first question in the hierarchy addresses energy use, given its importance to the financial performance and ongoing environmental impacts of a building. If a product has a measurable negative impact on building energy use, the decision rule is to eliminate or modify it. The next question addresses occupant health, then durability, and the attention then shifts to manufacturing. This approach is used to evaluate oriented strand-board sheating (OSB) as illustrated at right.

Architect William McDonough, a leader in green building from the early 1980s design of the Environmental Defense Fund's offices to the more recent $2 billion make-over of Ford Motor Company's River Rouge factory, has also developed a useful framework for materials selection. In partnership with industrial chemist Michael Braungart, McDonough has gone further. Deeply dissatisfied with current material choices, they created McDonough Braungart Design Chemistry, a product and systems development firm that assists clients in designing and redesigning everything from carpets to college campuses. In their book, *Cradle-to-cradle*, McDonough and Braungart outline their approach to selecting materials for product design. Concerned primarily with ecosystem toxicity and effects on human health, this approach can also be applied to selecting building products.[11]

Their approach involves assigning potential materials to an "X" or elimination list of those unacceptable under any circumstances (for example, PVC, cadmium, mer-

ORIENTED-STRAND BOARD SHEATHING

An application of EBN's Simplified Method to oriented-strand board (OSB) sheathing.

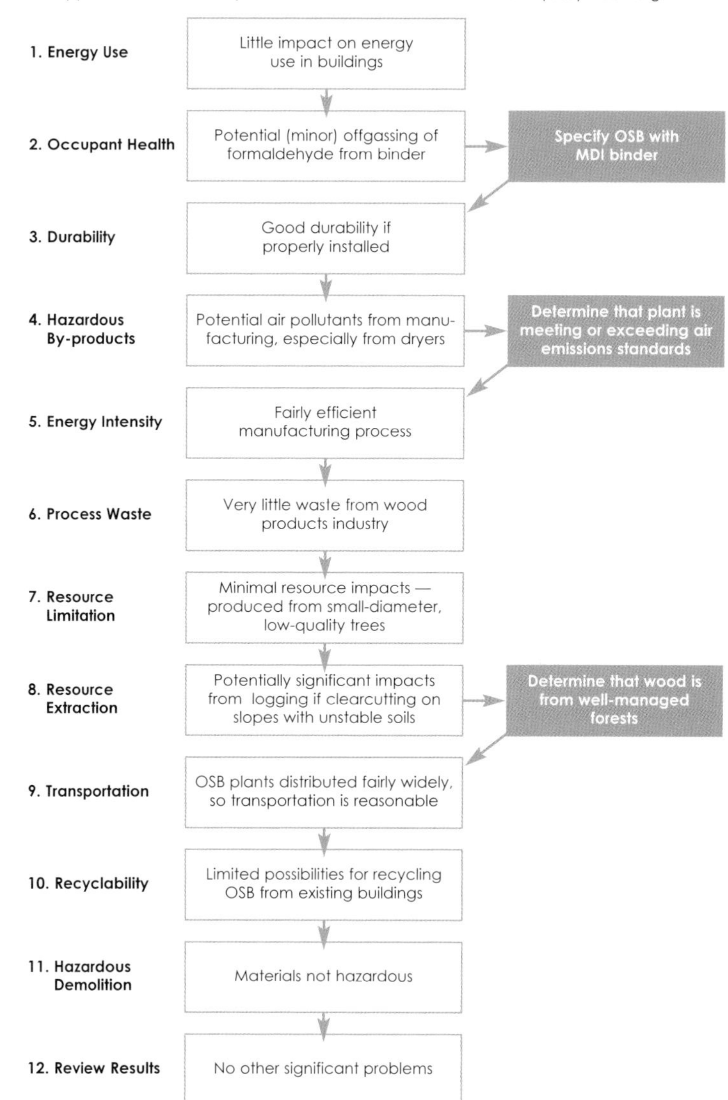

Source: *Environmental Building News (EBN)*, Vol. 6, #1, p. 13.

VIII

GLOBAL SUPPLY AND DEMAND FOR WOOD

The U.S. uses far more wood than any other country, most of it for construction. We can and should use our market power and influence to improve forest management, starting at home. ■

WOOD PROVIDED BY TOP 25 SUPPLIERS

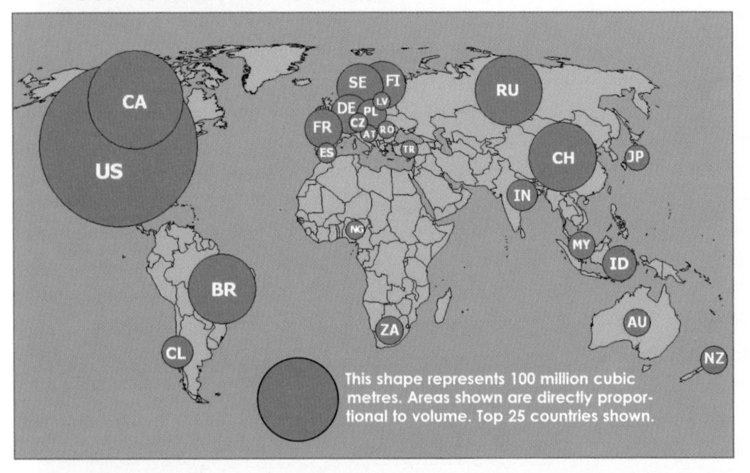

DEMAND FOR WOOD BY TOP 25 USERS

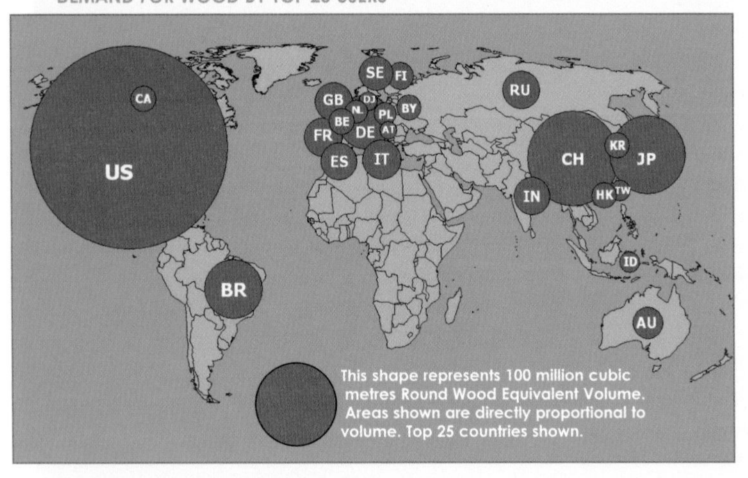

Source: Global Forest and Trade Network, WWF.

cury, and wood from endangered forests); a grey list which contains problematic substances that have no substitutes or are less dangerous than those on the X list (for example, cadmium is highly toxic, but continues to be used in the production of photovoltaic solar collectors); and a "P" or preferred list that contains substances that are actively defined as healthy, safe, or desirable. Given the dirth of information on the life-cycle costs and benefits of most materials, McDonough and Braungart advocate following informed personal choices. In addition, the current inventory of materials offers less than perfect choices — for example, should one choose a petrochemical-based fiber produced locally, a wool carpet imported from New Zealand with unknown habitat effect, or cotton produced with vast amounts of pesticides and water? The design team needs to develop decision rules to guide them through these "frying pan or fire" situations; for example, selecting natural fibers over petrochemical-based fibers, or deciding that habitat loss trumps local sourcing. However imperfect, this approach will lead to better decisions than throwing up one's hands when confronted with highly imperfect and conflicting information.

The next step is to put the list into action — eliminate the materials on the X list, minimize the materials on the grey list, and actively seek out materials on the preferred list. Finally, and most powerfully, the authors advocate reinvention — redefining the objective. For example, instead of designing a parking lot, one could imagine the task of designing alternative ways for tenants and visitors to access the building.

Chainsaw Conservation: The Case for Wood

Borrowing from these approaches and others, the Natural Capital Center building team developed its own framework based on our local and regional context, and Ecotrust's values and programmatic objectives. For example, our selection of FSC (Forest Stewardship Council) certified wood for the deck was guided by the predominance and importance of forests in the Pacific Northwest, and our interest in stimulating markets for FSC certified woods thereby encouraging more forests to be managed sustainably. A developer in a non-forested region wanting to reduce solid waste and create markets for plastics might just as reasonably have chosen recycled plastic lumber.

Life-cycle analysis and thinking can help bring a new perspective to resource questions. For example, many consumers see or hear about the effects of clearcutting forests and conclude that the best thing they can do for the environment is to reduce their use of wood. Some environmental groups and green builders have focused on developing strategies for minimizing wood use and recommending alternative building materials, such as concrete-clad wall systems. While reducing material use is always a good strategy, replacing wood with other materials may not be. First, in contrast to concrete or steel, wood is a renewable material. Forests store carbon and provide numerous other environmental services, such as filtering water and providing habitat. Second, wood products in the United States come from managed forests (harvests from public forests play an increasingly smaller role). Reducing demand is more likely to lead to conversion of forest land to development than it is to improved forest management. Third, wood is beautiful, naturally adding warmth and insulation. Fourth, life-cycle analyses comparing wood to steel and concrete indicate that wood is a far superior choice to concrete in terms of embodied energy, global warming potential, air and water toxicity, weighted resource use, and solid waste, and superior to steel along all these dimensions except solid waste (see Sample Life-cycle Analysis on page 91).[12]

Wood does falter — or can falter — in one important area: effects on landscape and habitat. Forest management that maximizes short-term fiber production — using herbicides, pesticides, and fertilizers which contaminate water; cutting trees early before the forest develops into good habitat; cutting on steep slopes that contributes to landslides and stream siltation; fragmenting the landscape — significantly compromises the health of the environment and of people.

Fortunately, there is a way to reduce these landscape effects, making wood a superior choice on the habitat dimension as well. This is of critical importance to Ecotrust, and is central to the recovery of threatened and endangered wild salmon which thrive in forested landscapes with clear water, shade, big trees, and diverse vegetation. Proving again that what is good for salmon is good for people, this approach to forestry, which emphasizes diversity and long rotations (for example, growing forests to 60–90 years rather than the industrial approach of 35–45 years prevalent in the Pacific Northwest), generally yields more wood, higher carbon storage, and greatly improved biodiversity relative to the current fiber-maximizing industrial model.[13] This approach to forestry, with more frequent but smaller harvests, also provides more stable employment, a departure from the boom and bust which has characterized the timber industry since its inception. Creating and maintaining this type of forest is consistent with the criteria of FSC certification, which emphasize long-term forest productivity, enhancing biodiversity, and providing for local livelihoods. Despite its clear benefits, few industrial

A snapshot of two working forests: the forest on the right, certified by the Forest Stewardship Council, provides wood through small patch cuts that retain the standing forest. The forest on the left reflects typical industrial management.

GLOBAL TRENDS IN FSC CERTIFIED FORESTLAND

Million acres
100
80
60
40
20
0
1995 1996 1997 1998 1999 2000 2001 2002

Source: Forest Stewardship Council.

PROCURING FSC CERTIFIED WOOD

The supply and availability of FSC wood continues to be limited, and market demand is critical to stimulate additional FSC certification by forest owners, mills, distributors, and secondary manufacturers. There are a number of strategies a building team can use to increase their success in procuring FSC wood:

- Early in the project, identify local vendors, suppliers, and manufacturers that carry FSC certified wood (the Certified Wood Product Association, www.cwpa.info, has a database that can be sorted by product, market, or supplier).

- Provide your wood list to project bidders and encourage them to contact certified vendors as early as possible to establish availability and pricing.

- Hold a workshop for your contractor and project bidders on FSC certification. The Certified Wood Product Association has resource materials and regional coordinators who can assist you in presentations. There are also a number of conservation organizations that provide knowledgeable staff and resources to facilitate FSC procurement, including Ecotrust in the Pacific Northwest, the Community Forestry Resource Center in Minnesota, and the Natural Resources Defense Council (NRDC) in San Francisco.

- Specify lower-grade wood; this will increase the chances that a certified supplier can provide it, and will also support improved forest management. The use of a larger variety of wood decreases "high-grading" (removing the most valuable trees which may also be valuable to leave standing as seed trees) and logging pressure on forests.

- Specify FSC certified wood separately for each application rather than a blanket approach applying to all wood products. Where FSC supply is limited, specify FSC certified materials in the primary bid and non-certified materials in the alternate bid.

- Require that project contractors and subcontractors submit vendor invoices containing their chain-of-custody certification numbers and identifying each certified product on a line-item basis. This is the only way to ensure that the product really originated in an FSC certified forest, and is required by LEED to obtain the FSC credit.

- Consider procuring certified wood in advance to hedge against changes in availability. If requested far enough in advance, wood can be reserved in a FSC certified forest for a particular project. ■

Source: Based on information from Environmental Building News 12:4 (April 2003) and *Wood for Building Green* produced by Metafore in 2003, which also contains sample specification language, certified wood bid compliance forms, a vendor reference list, and other useful information. This publication can be obtained from Metafore by visiting www.metafore.org.

forests in North America are FSC certified (with some notable exceptions, such as those owned by The Collins Companies, Mendocino Redwood, and Tembec).

The timber industry, alarmed by FSC's early growth and rapid adoption in Europe and elsewhere, developed an industry certification system called the Sustainable Forestry Initiative (SFI). This initiative encourages industry members to follow state and federal regulations and to document and improve their environmental practices. While seeking industry certification may improve some elements of forest management, the SFI certification criteria do little to address other key elements of forest health: creating older, structurally-complex and diverse forests. Recognizing these substantial differences in certification criteria, the U.S. Green Building Council and most local green building programs only recognize and reward FSC certified products in their scoring systems.

As a consequence of the timber industry's lack of support for the Forest Stewardship Council, there is very little FSC wood produced regionally, and the wood that is produced tends to come from small family-owned forests. Channeling this FSC wood from small, dispersed forests through mills and distributors, which must be chain-of-custody certified to FSC standards (meaning that the wood is appropriately segregated and traced) to a building site can be inefficient and expensive. Building market demand is critical to the success of FSC. This encourages progressive forest owners, mills and distributors to become FSC certified, and increases supply and milling and distribution efficiencies.

Market demand for solid wood is very centralized: commercial and residential building uses most of the solid wood produced in the United States, much of which is concentrated in the hands of large developers and high-volume residential builders. Thus the building industry (and their homeowner clients) have the market power to change the way forests are managed in this region by demanding wood from sustainably managed forests.

To help fuel this market demand, the Natural Capital Center goal was to purchase 100% FSC certified wood. Despite our best efforts, we fell short of this goal due to limited availability of some products in the market at the time (softwood plywood and specialized roof members). We did achieve a 66% purchasing goal, which earned a LEED™ credit (the minimum threshold is 50% of new wood purchases). However, to achieve this goal we were often compelled to buy wood from outside of the region, an ironic situation in the Pacific Northwest which is defined and surrounded by lush, productive forests. In the intervening three years since the Natural Capital Center's redevelopment, the availability of FSC wood and wood products (doors, windows, framing lumber, hardwood and softwood plywood) has begun to increase, stimulated largely by green building and LEED.

While wood purchasing is only one aspect of green building, it is disproportionately significant in its power to induce change: a single large building project can create sufficient demand to entice a family forest to become FSC certified, and a few projects will encourage progressive industrial forest companies to follow suit. We will then all share in the benefits: cleaner water, better habitat, greater carbon storage, a more beautiful landscape, more and higher quality wood, and better and more stable jobs and opportunities.

Conclusion

By focusing on aspects of green building that are locally significant, the building project can navigate the current sea of poor information and clamoring priorities, and make a worthy contribution to improving economic, social and environmental conditions. Strategic material selection can also contribute significantly to local and regional economic development: an emphasis on local and deconstructed materials can lead to significant local product and business creation. Recent research estimates that deconstruction activities, if fully integrated into the demolition and building industry, could generate about 200,000 jobs annually and return $1 billion worth of building materials to the U.S. economy.[14]

The materials we select are, for the most part, a permanent feature of our building. They will survive for decades, perhaps centuries. They will probably survive us. At the Natural Capital Center, each material is part of our experience and our story. As we walk through our building, they are a constant reminder of decisions good and bad, the inspired moments and the lapses in attention — captured in wood and concrete, in wallboard and insulation. They will continue to tell our story long after we are gone, a delight or a curse for future building occupants and owners. In the end, the materials we choose reflect the story we want to tell and the world we want to build. ■

by Eugénie Frerichs

If there is one thing that can be said with certainty about the Natural Capital Center, it is that after just under two years of existence in its rehabilitated state, the century-old warehouse is teeming with life. Towards the end of 2003 the building had received just over 400,000 visitors.[1] People shopping at Patagonia, eating at Hot Lips Pizza, heading to an event in the conference center on the second floor; curious passers-by dropping in on the "Wednesday at Noon" building tours; school groups, international delegates, or visitors meeting with any of the 25 tenants in the building all contributed to this large number. Hundreds of additional visitors undoubtedly went uncounted, wandering through the halls on their own, picking up literature, scanning the computers and books in the Conservation Economy Resource Library, puzzling over the moose head on the wall, or reading about one of the organizations housed within the building in the brochures stacked on the public shelves.

In addition to visitors, many of the 125 people who work in the building are often seen dashing from the third floor to the first floor and back up to the second to collaborate with other organizations in the building on new projects, meet guests downstairs for lunch, or to hold a meeting upstairs on the terrace where the air is fresh and the view expansive. The building buzzes with curiosity, creativity, and synergy.

The building's conference center has hosted over 800 events in two years, from workshops to weddings and fundraisers to movie screenings.

Designing for Community

This was no accident. Even during the earliest stages of the design process, we were interested in creating a space that encouraged such energy and productivity. Just as we valued the health and integrity of the building's greater urban ecosystem, we considered the building *itself* an ecosystem, one that required the same attention to diversity, adaptability, healthy inputs and outputs, and, ultimately, one that would feel *alive*. Too often a building's design will end on the last day of active construction, leaving tenants on their own to sort out how to create community and bring life to their new space. Instead, the Natural Capital Center's design team hoped to create physical spaces that would not be considered complete until real live human beings interacted with or responded to the space.

NATURAL CAPITAL CENTER BUILDING COUNCIL

The Natural Capital Center Building Council was established soon after the building opened. With representatives from most of the building tenants, the Council meets every other month in a casual environment to discuss and plan a variety of building-wide activities that fall under categories of both work and play. Subcommittees report their progress at the beginning of each meeting. The topics include energy purchasing and conservation, purchasing practices (seeking opportunities for "greening" office supplies), and upcoming events. The Building Council also provides opportunities to maximize the collaboration among the community of tenants, fostering such programs as building-wide recycling and composting, service-learning projects, and holiday events.

Outdoor movie nights are a regular summer event. Open and free to all, this event builds community and increases awareness of the building and of Ecotrust.

The Building Council intends to develop a Sustainability Report for the Natural Capital Center. At the end of each year, working with Ashforth Pacific, the Council will prepare a report that summarizes the annual performance of the building's green attributes, including energy and water consumption, tenant transportation habits, waste production, and other relevant topics, based on surveys and reviews of the utility bills. By illustrating annual conservation benchmarks for the building, the Sustainability Report will help encourage the building community to strive continually for improvements in resource efficiency and to enhance a healthy work atmosphere. It will be distributed to the building tenants and any other interested members of the general public, as well as posted on the Natural Capital Center website. ■

This intent, however, creates a bit of a conundrum: considering that the human element is constant — and constantly changing — the building's design, never really ends. Interactions remain unpredictable; the building team and its tenants can do nothing more than watch and participate in the building as a living laboratory.

Authors and facilitators Franklin Becker and Fritz Steele were extremely influential in laying out the groundwork for many of the Natural Capital Center's community-based design concepts. In their book, *Workplace by Design*, Becker and Steele discuss the importance of creating spaces that inspire rather than stifle the employees working there each day. They argue that the physical layout of a space can significantly influence a person's experience within that space, and that certain design measures maximize collaboration and synergy while others perpetuate hierarchies and isolation, and decrease productivity.

From their observations on workspace dynamics, Becker and Steele developed the concept of "organizational ecology," which has come to mean, "Looking at organizations in terms of how work and workers are convened in space and time and how those kinds of decisions both affect and are affected by decisions about... the design of work processes and the organization's philosophy and values." They continue, "Our interest in the ecology of the place stems in large part from observing how difficult, but important, it is to think of the workplace as a single integrated system, not as a box filled with different parts."[2]

With these guiding principles in mind, Becker and Steele led a small group, including members of the building team and prospective tenants of the Natural Capital Center, through a design charette in the winter of 1999 that offered what to this day many of the participants praise as some of the most enlightening moments of the entire design process. Through a flurry of group discussions and hands-on brainstorming, the group answered — in a very brief period of time — several important questions about the building's interior spaces. Many of these questions also involved the arrangement of the private and public spaces. Details found throughout the Natural Capital Center today manifest the outcome of that day-long charette.

Of primary importance to the charette participants was the ability to inspire community, creativity, and collaboration among all of the tenants. Wandering through the building, one now notices several successful examples of this:

1. Many open spaces are left undefined, allowing for spontaneous interactions during which tenants determine the appropriate purpose of the space at that given moment.

2. Small meeting spaces appear in unusual nooks and crannies where project teams can temporarily disappear for uninterrupted brainstorming.

3. Artwork from local and contemporary artists is on display in all of the public spaces for inspiration and conversation.

4. Generous display niches are scattered throughout the building and changed regularly to reflect different themes of the conservation economy.

5. Areas of refuge from the office buzz are included on every floor; the outdoor terrace, fireplace, and comfortable seating areas throughout enable employees to take time for refueling and to clear their minds.

6. Employees from separate offices interact with each other regularly in the shared kitchens, meeting rooms, supply rooms, restrooms, and lounge areas, giving rise to new ideas discussed in a casual environment rather than in more formal conference rooms.

7. Views and natural lighting are available to some degree for every employee since most workstations are oriented around the outer perimeter of the building, where there are operable windows.

COMMUNITY SPACES IN THE NATURAL CAPITAL CENTER

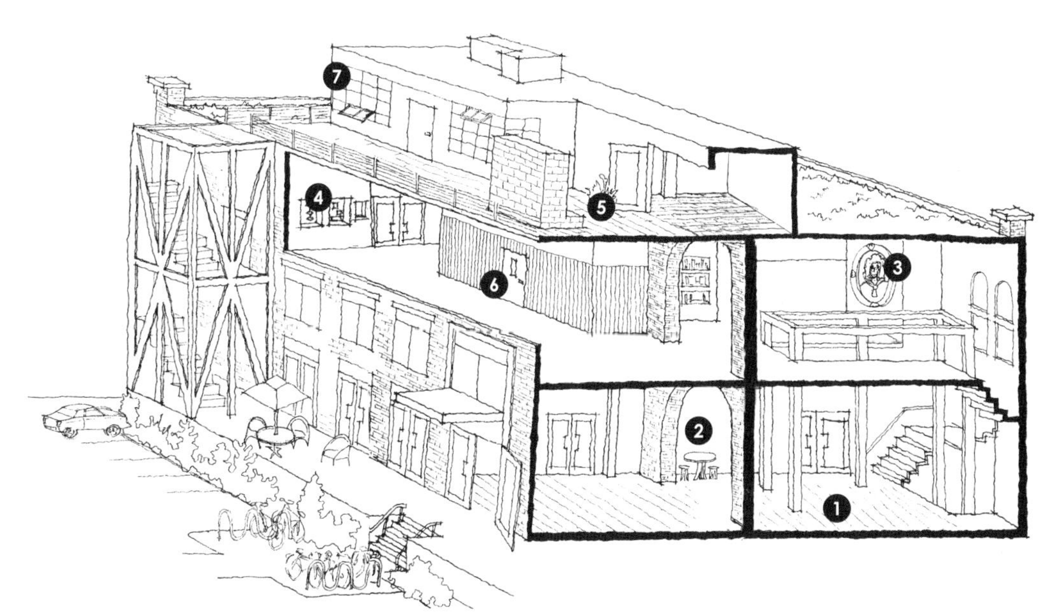

Additionally, individual workspaces in several of the offices are flexible in design, allowing for both privacy and openness, so that employees aren't confined to perpetual isolation or constant distraction. The flexibilty also enables changes in the workplace, such as growth or restructuring, to happen with ease. Similarly, concepts of office hierarchy diminish in areas where the "corner office" and the "executive suites" are not included in the layout. Instead, workstations are clustered in teams, and management works in tandem with the other project members.

THE PERILS OF COMMUNAL LIVING

Working in an open, communal atmosphere has a unique set of challenges. The open workspaces in the Natural Capital Center are quite literally just that: wide open. There are no more than five enclosed, private offices in the entire three-story building. With the creativity, collaboration, and immense teamwork the open workspaces foster, comes distraction, interruptions, and little space or time for long interludes of focused concentration or privacy. Some tenants moving into the building from more conventional work environments were apprehensive about the openness, and concerned not only about noise but also the privacy and security of office documents and personal belongings.

The faith in human nature that supported much of the design's shared, public spaces has been compromised on more than one occasion. Computers and flat screens have been stolen from the Resource Library and the atrium; the basement and restrooms have occasionally become temporary havens for local homeless people; and large events hosted in the building have resulted in damage to the outdoor terrace fireplace, the carpet, the bathrooms, or the paint on the interior walls.

So why does the building continue steadfastly down this open course? Perhaps because Ecotrust recognized from the beginning that there would be a price to pay for setting up such an open building in the middle of an urban landscape. The key has been, and will always be, not to overreact to these events, but to resolve each conflict on a case-by-case basis. Thus, in the offices, employees might bring headphones for the times when they need isolation, moveable dividers are available for those who need to close off their space for a while, and small private phone rooms and meeting spaces offer respite and privacy for phone calls and uninterrupted conversation. The missing computers have been replaced, flat screens mounted with security bolts, security presence heightened when public events are large, and after business hours access to the top two floors of the building is limited to employees only.

Yet the benefits of the open aspects of the building's design still outweigh the perils, and for every obstacle we have encountered there has been a more significant moment of understanding. Each added measure of security or privacy has proven manageable, and most importantly, has provided a teachable (and eventually laughable) moment. Ecotrust and the other tenants have taken these lessons to heart, and rather than prompting us to abandon community efforts, the challenges have strengthened the community's cohesiveness. Undoubtedly there will be more challenges to come; however, it will be far more enjoyable and far more useful to take them in stride, than to abandon our original intentions. It is, after all, a living laboratory. Occasionally the beaker explodes. ■

Hiking the Building

From the *Workplace by Design* charette, the life of the Natural Capital Center continues to evolve. The first floor atrium now functions as the building's nexus of activity, with a large skylight overhead showering light down onto an open area scattered with tables, a computer posting the latest news of the rainforest coast on Tidepool.org, a flat screen displaying a slide show or documentary video, Douglas-fir columns plastered with flyers of upcoming events, and traces of each retail business spilling out onto the floor. Here, visitors can pick up a *Field Guide to the Natural Capital Center* and take themselves on a self-guided tour of the building. A podium announces the events for the week in the conference center, and a stairway tucked in the eastern corner of the atrium invites visitors to wander upstairs and discover the rest of the building.

The development of an interpretive trail and the *Field Guide* were integral to engaging the general public in the daily life of the building. Produced by Ecotrust's communications and graphic design team, the *Field Guide* is free to any interested visitors. Beginning on the ground level, where the guides are displayed beneath a "Welcome" sign crafted from salvaged Douglas fir, the tour leads visitors through the entire building, peeking into work areas, peering up at the skylights, wandering down the hallways, and taking in views from the terrace, explaining all along the way the Natural Capital Center's strategies for transportation, energy, materials, community, water, and so on. Each descriptive page in the guide is matched with an engraved steel icon installed in or around the building. The interpretive trail's meandering format effectively opens the entire building up to the visiting public, expanding the building's community beyond its tenants to include anyone who enters its doors or enjoys its public spaces.

Once a building is designed as a private space, it is very hard to try to open it to the public at a later date. Committing to an interpretive trail up-front allowed us to plan for public interaction from the very beginning. We were able to incorporate other public design elements such as the interpretive display areas in the long corridors of the second floor, the Wild Salmon Center's aquarium filled with different species of Pacific salmon, and the strategic placement of artwork and tenant work samples in other areas that anticipated higher levels of foot traffic.

Selecting the Cast of Characters

If one thinks about a building as an ecosystem, diversity is essential to its long-term health and resilience. We wanted the Natural Capital Center to be a living, tangible ecosystem made up of a diverse network of organizations that manifested and supported the conservation economy. For-profit retail businesses and restaurants, non-profits, foundations, financial institutions, a trade association, a public agency — the tenants were assembled gradually, each a unique participant in our vision of a building where the concepts of ecology, economy, and social equity are intertwined. (See The Community of Tenants on page 108.)

It has been an enlightening experience for both tenants and visitors alike to learn about the many ways organizations can contribute to the development of a new marketplace: clothing made from organic fibers or recycled plastics; holistic health care; fairly traded coffee and tea; pizza whose toppings reflect seasonal, locally grown produce; pizza ovens that send waste heat directly to water heaters; financial lending that supports emerging entrepreneurs with environmentally sustainable businesses; a mutual fund that screens the environmental track record of its twenty-one companies; foundations supporting children, innovators, and inventors; non-profit conservation organizations advocating for healthy watersheds, sustainably-harvested timber, and the widespread use of native plants in landscaping; a City of Portland office wholly committed to green building, energy conservation, and solid waste and recycling. The list is vast and varied. One significant feature these businesses and organizations share is the belief that creating a new kind of marketplace does not require totally dismantling the previous model. Instead, the Natural Capital Center and its tenants provide tangible, real-life examples of this new way of thinking in forms that will be familiar to anyone who enters the bulding. The fine print, however, reveals exactly what is new and different — the commitment to social and ecological health working in tandem to support more traditional economic goals.

The alacrity with which collaborations emerged among the tenants was unexpected. Even before moving in, World Cup Coffee on the first floor was meeting with Sustainable Harvest, an importer of organic, fair trade, and shade grown coffees that moved in on the second floor, to discuss traveling together on a buying trip. Hot Lips Pizza and World Cup Coffee quickly became the first choice for catered events in the conference center, and for lunch and dinner meetings for many of the tenants. Once a month, all of the retailers on the first floor meet to compare foot traffic reports and develop joint marketing ventures that will strengthen their business presence in the rapidly growing River District. Their pro-

Shauna Alexander and Dave Griswold of Sustainable Harvest Coffee Co., "cupping," or tasting, coffee samples for quality control. They regularly hold cuppings in the second floor kitchen.

THE COMMUNITY OF TENANTS

First Floor

Patagonia
Environmentally conscious makers of quality outdoor clothing, Patagonia is known for its recycled fleece and organic cotton garments and for its support of grassroots environmental groups. *www.patagonia.com*

World Cup Coffee
Featuring a selection of organic teas and shade grown coffees, World Cup opened its second Portland café in the Natural Capital Center.
www.worldcupcoffee.com

Hot Lips Pizza
Using local and organically grown ingredients as the mainstay of their seasonal menu, Hot Lips Pizza — a favorite at the Portland farmer's markets — opened its third location in the Natural Capital Center.
www.hotlipspizza.com

The Pearl Clinic and Pharmacy
The Pearl Clinic offers an innovative approach to health and wellness by emphasizing the appropriate use of conventional and alternative medicine. *www.pearlclinic.com*

Second Floor

Ecotrust
Ecotrust is a non-profit organization dedicated to building Salmon Nation, a place where people and wild salmon thrive. Ecotrust seeks economic solutions to environmental and community problems. *www.ecotrust.org*

Wild Salmon Center
Dedicated to research and conservation of wild salmon, trout, steelhead, and their ecosystems along the Pacific Rim, the Wild Salmon Center works to protect the last, best places for these native fish. *www.wildsalmoncenter.org*

Progressive Investment Management
With offices in Portland, Eugene, and Seattle, Progressive helps thousands of private clients to discover the benefits of investing intelligently and responsibly. *www.progressiveinvestment.com*

ShoreBank Pacific
The nation's first environmental bank, ShoreBank Pacific offers EcoDeposit accounts to individuals, organizations, and businesses, and is dedicated to

small business lending that builds a conservation economy in communities of the Pacific Northwest. *www.sbpac.com*

Sustainable Harvest
One of the leading North American importers of organic, shade-grown, and fairly traded specialty coffees, Sustainable Harvest sells to coffee roasters and natural food supermarkets in the U.S. and Canada.
www.sustainableharvest.com

Individual Tree Selection Management
This consulting forestry company provides forest management services for private and public land owners and is a certified resource manager under the guidelines of the Forest Stewardship Council.

The Bill Healy Foundation
A private foundation funding projects that focus on children and the environment in Oregon and Hawaii.
www.billhealyfoundation.org

The Lemelson Foundation
A private philanthropy that creates and supports programs to encourage inventors and innovators.
www.lemelson.org

Tillamook Rainforest Coalition
The Tillamook Rainforest Coalition is a unique group of anglers, commercial fishermen, conservationists, landowners, and others working to inspire Oregonians to protect the health of the Tillamook and Clatsop State Forests. *www.tillamookrainforest.org*

The Conservation Fund
Rated by both Worth and Forbes magazines as one of the nation's top charities, the Conservation Fund works to forge partnerships to preserve America's legacy of wildlife habitat, working landscapes and community open-space.
www.conservationfund.org

Interforest
Dedicated to increasing the value and improving the management of forest properties worldwide, Interforest provides integrated consulting, focusing their services on resource management strategy development, organizational and leadership development, and survey research and public involvement strategies.
www.iforest.com

Third Floor

Metafore
Formerly part of the Certified Forest Products Council, Metafore's mission is to conserve, protect and restore the world's forests by promoting responsible forest products buying practices throughout North America.
www.certifiedwood.com

The Certified Wood and Paper Association
The CWPA serves the green building community by delivering services and developing markets for independently certified wood and paper products from well-managed forests and from recycled-content and reclaimed/rediscovered sources. *www.cwpa.info*

The Environmental Careers Organization
A non-profit education, training, and leadership organization committed to the development of environmental professionals. *www.eco.org*

Naito Development LLC
Naito Development specializes in commercial development and historic rehabilitation in Portland.
www.naitodev.com

Oregon Disability Sports
ODS provides and promotes sports, recreation and fitness activities for youth and adults with physical disabilities. *www.oregondisabilitysports.org*

Plantnative.com
A web-based center for native plants and beneficial landscaping resources.
www.plantnative.com

Sageworks Media
Provides educational media products on issues of health, livability and social justice.

City of Portland's Office of Sustainable Development
The leader of Portland's energy, solid waste and recycling, green building and sustainability efforts, the Office of Sustainability is internationally recognized for its innovative and progressive civic leadership.
www.sustainableportland.org

Cascadia Region Green Building Council
Cascadia Region Green Building Council builds capacity for sustainable buildings and communities in Oregon, Washington and British Columbia. An inaugural Chapter of US Green Building Council and the first Chapter to have its own staff, Cascadia is the newest tenant in the building.

GREEN HOUSEKEEPING

New research from the U.S. Geological Survey indicates that many household products in daily use are contaminating rivers and streams. As the scientific tools for detecting these contaminants have become more sophisticated, studies have revealed that a startling number of compounds are being discharged into the natural environment with unforeseen or unknown impacts. In addition to pharmaceuticals such as steroids, reproductive hormones, antiobiotics, and other drugs, substances such as caffeine, detergents, disinfectants, fragrances, insect repellents, fire retardants, and plasticizers are turning up in aquatic systems.

Despite this developing understanding of the risks of toxic chemicals to the environment, and existing knowledge of human health risks related to chemical exposure, typical commercial buildings are cleaned with products containing numerous hazardous ingredients. More often than not, the standard cleaners available contain dangerous compounds such as glycol ether, linear alcohol from crude oil, butyl, caustics, chlorine, borine, phosphorus, nonyl phenol, phenols, quaternaries, silicone, known carcinogens, and other undesirable compounds.

Fortunately, a range of non-toxic products is increasingly available. These products are made with natural cleaning agents such as citrus extracts and vinegar, live enzyme cultures, corn and coconut bases, botanical extracts, vegetable fiber, minerals, vitamins, aloe, soybean, cider vinegar, meadow foam seeds, and white cedar leaf extracts. These solutions can be equally effective, yet do not contain carcinogens and ozone depleting substances, and they do not compromise the health of janitorial staff, building occupants, or the environment.

The Natural Capital Center is cleaned with a line of earth-friendly solutions made by an Oregon company, Bi-O-Kleen.™ The products use grapefruit seed and pulp extract, a natural compound well known for its effectiveness as a safe, alternative bactericide, fungicide, antiviral, antiparasitic, preservative, and antioxidant. This ingredient is non-toxic, non-irritant, and non-corrosive. Bi-O-Kleen is locally produced and highly concentrated, reducing shipping impacts, and the product containers can be returned for reuse, eliminating packaging wastes.

In addition to cleaning solutions, paper products in all restrooms are 100% recycled and contain 40% post-consumer waste. Though white, these paper products are bleached with an environmentally sound hydrogen peroxide process, not chlorine. The purchase of recycled products with post-consumer content helps stimulate the market for recycled fibers — a significant part of the waste stream for any office building. ■

— Lisa Miles, Sustainability Coordinator, Ashforth Pacific

motions have been creative, events-based marketing ideas such as the establishment of *Postal Service Appreciation Week*. Every November, the roughly 1500 employees of Portland's Main Post Office located across the street, are invited by Natural Capital Center businesses to receive exclusive discounts and special offers, that range from free pizza and frisbees to discounts on prescriptions and coffee refills. Other promotions include building-wide First Thursday[3] events, shared sponsorship of the streetcar stop near the west entrance to the building, and special holiday season promotions for Natural Capital Center tenants.

Maintaining the Momentum

History has proven that, despite a design team's sincere efforts and choreographic innovation with interior space, good intentions alone will not ensure a thriving community several years down the road. To avoid establishing of a community whose buzz fizzles when the initial enthusiasm dies, Ecotrust allocated special funding to support a team of permanent, committed staff members whose sole responsibility is to ensure that the Natural Capital Center remains a lively, vibrant community for many years to come. The team consists of the Natural Capital Center Programs Manager, Ecotrust's Events Coordinator, and the Natural Capital Center Building Council, which is comprised of representatives from several of the building's tenants (see **Natural Capital Center Building Council** on page 104).

Working closely with Ecotrust's internal team is Ashforth Pacific, a professional property management company that oversees all of the operations and maintenance for the Natural Capital Center. Ashforth Pacific is no ordinary property management company. Based in Portland, the company is a sustaining member of the Oregon Natural Step Network, and since 1997 has followed a company-wide environmental initiative that focuses on lessening the impact of its properties' everyday activities. For increased efficiency in energy and water consumption, the company retrofits its properties with low-energy lights, installs lighting controls, modifies the HVAC systems, and installs aerators on all faucets and showerheads. It has selected landscaping and cleaning supplies that are chemical free and non-polluting, and is a staunch supporter of its neighborhood public transportation options. In 2002, Ashforth Pacific was honored at Portland's BEST Business Awards (Businesses for an Environmentally Sustainable Tomorrow) for its overall success at integrating these environmental initiatives into daily operations and for being a leader in the business community that challenges itself and others to explore and develop creative new approaches to well established business practices.

Because of its commitment to green property management, we selected Ashforth Pacific to take on the invaluable task of ensuring that the principles of green building that emerged during the Natural Capital Center's design remain vital in its day-to-day operations. Ashforth representatives work closely with Ecotrust to ensure that the electrical systems remain efficient, water is conserved, cleaning and landscaping are chemical-free, the building is safe and secure, and tenants are regularly informed of the building's operations. Ashforth Pacific also works closely with the Natural Capital Center's Building Council on new ventures such as a building-wide composting program, a purchasing plan for renewable energy, and increased efforts to facilitate recycling.

With daily building operations well in the hands of Ashforth Pacific, the Natural Capital Center Programs Manager focuses on the community-based aspects of the building management. In conjunction with the Events Coordinator, the Programs Manager works tirelessly to promote, schedule, and manage all open spaces in the building, to coordinate building tours, and to manage the hundreds of events that are held regularly either in the first floor atrium, the 2,000 square foot conference center on the second floor or, in the summer months, on the 3,000 square foot third floor terrace. The Manager makes all curatorial decisions concerning displays and interpretive material throughout the building, and helps to create and maintain a sense of community among tenants by staying in close contact, and keeping up to date on recent campaigns, partnerships, or new marketing ventures. In effect, the Natural Capital Center Programs Manager operates as the Mayor of the Natural Capital Center.

Staying abreast of all of the activities in the Natural Capital Center is no small task. Generous public spaces occupy large portions of each level of the building, where non-profits, businesses, and private parties hold events ranging in size from 15 to 300 participants (see A Sampling of Events on page 112). In 2002 alone, roughly 13,000 people came to the Natural Capital Center to attend a workshop, meeting, or reception in the conference center, the atrium, or on the third floor terrace. Events held in the Natural Capital Center function not only as forums in which like-minded organizations can brainstorm and disseminate their ideas and actions, but also as outreach tools, drawing in visitors who may have never heard of the building project or its intentions.

The events in the Natural Capital Center also carry an additional, less altruistic responsibility, namely income generation. There are many financial costs associated with community development. For Ecotrust, these costs include two full-time, salaried positions, a state-of-the-art conference center, and round-the-clock

Wally Verbeck, the building's maintenance specialist, showing off the Natural Capital Center's non-toxic cleaning supplies.

The Oregon Bus Project

The Natural Capital Center overflowed with enthusiastic young rabble-rousers when the Oregon Bus Project hosted both its kick-off and closing celebrations in the building in 2002. Founded by young political activists, the Oregon Bus Project's mission is: "To educate ourselves and bridge the urban-suburban-rural divide; to engage a new generation of progressive leaders; to revive progressive politics in the Oregon legislature." [www.secretplan.org]

Slow Food Portland, Salone Northwest

Slow Food Portland, the local chapter of Slow Food U.S.A., a non-profit educational organization dedicated to the enjoyment of ecological and regional culinary traditions, held a weekend-long series of workshops, tastings, and discussions that filled the Natural Capital Center with aromas of regional and Italian wines, cheeses, cured meats, and balsamic vinegars. [www.slowfoodusa.org]

ReThink Series

In the spring of 2003, the City of Portland's Green Building program and Metro, the regional government, co-hosted a workshop series called Rethink: Innovation in ecological design and construction. The sold-out sixteen week course presented the latest information, challenges, and inspiration behind the rapidly growing green building movement. Participants received professional certificates and AIA credits for attending the workshops, which will return again in 2004. [www.green-rated.org]

TACS (Technical Assistance for Community Service)

For more than twenty-five years, TACS has provided resources and capacity building assistance for thousands of non-profit organizations working in Oregon and Washington. TACS was one of the first clients of the conference center, hosting daylong workshops and morning network meetings for regional non-profits, focusing on management-level issues, financial management, diversity, fund development, marketing, and information technology. [www.tacs.org]

Round River Conservation Studies: Pacific Salmon Research Update

A collection of regional fisheries biologists and conservationists convened in the conference center for an intensive day reviewing the status of salmon research in the Pacific Northwest. [www.roundriver.org] ■

attention from an external management company, not to mention the calculated loss of revenue (every square foot given up to public space accounts for approximately $20 per year of lease revenue). Therefore we have arranged to have the events help sustain our building program. Revenue generated from renting the event spaces feeds directly into the operational budget for the community-building programs. Continued efforts to invite the public into the building will only increase the financial and programmatic paybacks. Plans for 2003-2004 include using the building as a pick-up site for subscribers to a local organic farm, and as the northwest Portland location for the Portland Farmer's Market, which occurs every Thursday evening during summer months. Event scheduling in the building is rising, with break-even forecasts for as soon as 2004. (For more on associated costs, see the The Perils of Communal Living on page 106.)

With an increasing number of activities and events in the Natural Capital Center comes a steady flow of new visitors from around the region, if not the world. These visitors are perhaps the final and most critical ingredient in the building's recipe for community, for they play the role of harbinger. Anyone who enters the Natural Capital Center becomes an active participant in the conservation economy, by supporting tenant businesses and organizations, being exposed to the latest ideas, issues, trials, and triumphs of this bioregion, or simply sitting in the atrium, reading a book, and feeling inspired. After their stop, be it brief or momentous in their everyday experience, visitors return to their own worlds with new stories to share. Thus some of the ideas of this diverse community of tenants may spread well beyond the small city of Portland. This is already beginning to happen — the building is capturing international attention and hosting visitors from Peru to Yemen.

Conclusion

Entering its second year, the building is still settling into its new identity, and life here continues to evolve. We hope it will always be this way. With each lesson learned — how to fight harder for installing rain cisterns, when to not use permeable asphalt, when to buy security bolts for computers — Ecotrust makes a note and passes it along. We are encouraging those embarking on similar projects around the Northwest and beyond to view this redevelopment as but one among many: a project that offers a few ideas and suggestions for changing how buildings are designed, built, and inhabited. Perhaps 15 years from now no one will be talking about the Natural Capital Center because its attributes will have become commonplace and overshadowed by dozens of others that push the ideas of energy conservation to higher limits, whose water use and reuse flows in a completely closed loop, or whose community of tenants buzzes with so much synergy and enthusiasm that neighbors complain of the noise. Perhaps fifteen years from now a green building filled with life, and with economy, community, and ecology completely intertwined, will be old news. There are worse things. ■

NOTES

Chapter 2

1. Peter Calthorpe and William Fulton, *The Regional City: Planning for the End of Sprawl* (Washington, D.C.: Island Press, 2001).
2. Energy Information Administration, *Monthly Energy Review* (Washington, D.C.: U.S. Department of Energy, March 2001) and Energy Information Administration, *Emissions of Greenhouse Gases in the United States, 1999* (Washington, D.C.: U.S. Department of Energy, October 2000).
3. U.S. Environmental Protection Agency, *A Characterization of Building-Related Construction and Demolition Debris in the United States* (Washington, D.C.: U.S. EPA, 1998).
4. Cramer-Kresselt Research, "Facilities and Real Estate Strategies" (paper prepared for the National Summit on Building Performance, November 1996).
5. David Malin Roodman and Nicholas Lenssen, *A Building Revolution: How Ecology and Health Concerns Are Transforming Construction*, Worldwatch Paper 124 (Washington, D.C.: Worldwatch, 1995).
6. Timothy Beatley, *Green Urbanism: Learning from European Cities* (Washington, D.C.: Island Press, 2000).
7. Information on economic returns was gleaned from authors' personal correspondence with Dennis Wilde, Gerding Edlen Development; Lucia Athens, City of Seattle; and Peter Busby, Busby and Associates, as well as from A. Wilson, et al., *Green Development: Integrating Ecology and Real Estate* (New York: John Wiley and Sons, 1998).
8. Paul Hawken, Amory Lovins, and Hunter L. Lovins, *Natural Capitalism* (Boston: Little, Brown, and Co., 1999). This is also the direct experience of Portland, Oregon's utility company, Portland General Electric.
9. Seattle City Light, *Sustainable Demand Project Final Report-High Performance Building Delivers Results* (Seattle: Seattle City Light, 2001) found online at www.cityofseattle.net/light/conserve/sustainability/SDPFRa.pdf; and Rocky Mountain Institute, *Green Development: Integrating Ecology and Real Estate* (New York: John Wiley & Sons, Inc., 1998).
10. J.J. Romm and W.D Browning, *Greening the Building and the Bottom Line: Increasing Productivity Through Energy-Efficient Design*, Rocky Mountain Institute Publication #D94-27 (Snowmass, Colorado: Rocky Mountain Institute, 1994).
11. Athena Steen, Bill Steen, and David Eisenberg, *The Straw Bale House* (White River Junction, Vermont: Chelsea Green Publishing Co., 1994).

Chapter 3

1. Portions of text used with permission from Metafore's, *Wood for Building Green*, 2003 Edition which can be obtained through its website www.metafore.org.

Chapter 4

1. Jane Jacobs, *The Death and Life of Great American Cities* (New York: Vintage Books, 1961).
2. Clem Labine, "Preservationists Are Un-American," *Historic Preservation* vol. 31, no. 1 (March/April 1979): 18–20.
3. Jane Jacobs, *The Death and Life of Great American Cities* (New York: Vintage Books, 1961).
4. Statistics can be found on the National Park Service's website page on Federal Historic Preservation Tax Incentives: www2.cr.nps.gov/tps/tax/tax_p.htm.
5. Standards can be found in 36 CFR (Code of Federal Regulations) Part 67 or online at www2.cr.nps.gov/tps/tax/rehabstandards.htm.

Chapter 5

1. The Portland Development Commission's River District Development Map can be found online at www.pdc.us/gfx/proj/river/river_district_ura.gif.
2. See the Energy Efficient Mortgage Home Owner Guide at www.pueblo.gsa.gov/cic_text/housing/energy_mort/energy-mortgage.htm

Chapter 6

1. Energy and Environmental Analysis, Inc. (EEA), *Breathing Easier About Energy: A Healthy Economy and Healthier Air* (Washington, DC: Foundation for Clean Air Progress, January 2002). Report can be found online at: www.cleanairprogress.org/report_energy/united_states.pdf.
2. The production of cement used in buildings, which releases a significant amount of greenhouse gases, also contributes to the 40% figure.
3. Text adapted from the website of the non-profit organization Fuel Cells 2000; www.fuelcells.org.
4. Ian Theaker, P. Eng. (Interface Engineering) and Paul Schwer, P.E. (PAE Consulting Engineering), "Natural Ventilation for the Pacific Northwest" (paper presented at the City of Portland Office of Sustainable Development — Green Building Division's ReThink: Innovation in Ecological Design and Construction, Portland, March 2003).

5. Some facts derived from Donald Dawson, "Plant-Covered Roofs Ease Urban Heat," *National Geographic News* (Washington, D.C.: November 15, 2002). This article can also be found at http://news.nationalgeographic.com).

6. More details on the BETC program and the solar income calculation can be found online at www.energy.state.or.us/bus/tax/sustain.htm.

Chapter 7

1. This inscription was written by Joel Weinstein in 1993.

2. Alex Wilson, "Cleaning Up Stormwater: Understanding Pollutant Removal from Runoff," *Environmental Building News* 11:2 (February, 2002): 12.

3. Statistics from the Portland Bureau of Environmental Services website: www.cleanrivers-pdx.org.

4. In 2003, students from Portland State University will be implementing a series of tests to monitor exact quantities of stormwater flowing from the roof into the swales. Ecotrust does not have these figures yet.

5. It is important to assess the soil structure of the building site before including any infiltration strategies. Some sites may have too much sand or clay, or be too contaminated. The Natural Capital Center did not have any problems like these.

6. The remaining 5% is from two downspouts on the eastern side of the green roof that had to be directed into the city's pipes. It was not possible to create a channel that would connect these outlets with the rest of the building's system on the western side of the lot.

7. The first park is Jamison Park, located between Northwest 10th & 11th Avenues, and Irving and Johnson Streets.

8. A detailed account of Napa's restoration project is available in Gretchen C. Daily and Katherine Ellison, *The New Economy of Nature: The Quest to Make Conservation Profitable* (Washington, D.C.: Shearwater Books, 2002).

Chapter 8

1. Pete Lewis, "Deconstructing green," *Natural Business LOHAS Journal* (May/June 2001): 21-24.

2. Linda Logan, "Stroke of Brilliance," *Natural Home* (May/June 2001): 61–62.

3. For a summary of life cycle analysis tools, please see Nadav Malin, "Life-cycle assessments for buildings: seeking the holy grail," *Environmental Building News* 11:3, (March 2002): 1, 8–15.

4. See www.iso.org, and follow the links to ISO 14040, the standard that addresses life-cycle analysis.

5. Malin, "Life-cycle assessment for buildings: seeking the holy grail," 9.

6. Ibid., 9.

7. Ibid., 10.

8. Peter Yost, "Deconstruction: back to the future for buildings?," *Environmental Building News* 9:5 (May 2000): 10.

9. Metro Regional Management Department, *The construction industry recycling toolkit: a directory of recycling and salvage operations 2002–2003* (Portland, Oregon: Metro, 2003).

10. Nadav Malin and Alex Wilson, "Materials selection: tools, resources, and techniques for choosing green," *Environmental Building News* 6:1 (January 1997): 1, 10–14.

11. William McDonough and Michael Braungart, *Cradle to cradle: remaking the way we make things* (New York: North Point Press, 2002).

12. Dr. Robert Kozak and Dr. Christopher Gaston, "Life-cycle analysis" (paper presented at the Workshop on Climate Change, Carbon, and Forestry, Orcas Island, Washington, November 13–16, 2001).

13. Andrew B. Carey, Bruce R. Lippke, and John Sessions, "Intentional Systems Management: Managing Forests for Biodiversity," *Journal of Sustainable Forestry* 9 (3/4) (1999): 83–124.

14. See www.ilsr.org/recycling/ for statistics on deconstruction, job creation, and value generation.

Chapter 9

1. Based on surveys and tallies tracked by Ecotrust.

2. Franklin Becker and Fritz Steele, *Workplace by Design: Mapping the High-Performance Workscape* (San Francisco: Jossey-Bass, Inc., 1995).

3. First Thursday is a tradition in Portland, and is particularly popular in the River District, the neighborhood around the Natural Capital Center. On the first Thursday of each month, galleries stay open into the evening with new art shows, and the streets are filled with vendors, live music, and entertainment.

CONTRIBUTORS

Spencer B. Beebe
Preface

Spencer Beebe founded Ecotrust in February 1991 and has served as President since its inception. After 13 years with The Nature Conservancy as Northwest representative, Western Regional Director, Vice President and President of the Nature Conservancy's International Program, he was the Founding President of Conservation International in 1987. Spencer earned his M.F.S. (Forest Science) degree in 1974 from Yale University's School of Forestry and Environmental Studies, a B.A. in Economics from Williams College in 1968, and honorary doctors of law from Williams College and New England College. He served with the Peace Corps in Honduras from 1968–71. In addition to his work with Ecotrust, Spencer serves on the Boards of a variety of national and international conservation and development organizations including Shorebank Corporation, Shorebank Pacific, Ecotrust Canada, and the Craighead Wildlife Wildlands Institute.

Rob Bennett
The Case for Green Building

Rob Bennett has been active in community development and environmental planning for over a decade. In 1997 he joined the City of Portland's Office of Sustainable Development, coordinating the city's green building and neighborhood-based conservation programs. Prior to working for the City, Rob was a community organizer with Neighbors West/Northwest and worked with a variety of public agencies and not-for-profit organizations including Tri-Met, Portland Office of Transportation, The Center for Rural Massachusetts, and Massachusetts Rural Development Council. Rob is currently manager of the City of Portland's internationally renowned Green Building Division, where he oversees program and policy development for the G/Rated program. Rob is a graduate of the University of Massachusetts-Amherst School of Landscape Architecture and Regional Planning and the University of Richmond. He sits on the boards of the U.S. Green Building Council's Cascadia Chapter and REACH Community Development, both based in Portland, Oregon.

Stuart Cowan
The Case for Green Building

Stuart Cowan served as the Conservation Economy Research Director at Ecotrust from 1999–2002. In that time his team developed a groundbreaking framework for bioregional sustainability, which provides a visual "pattern language" integrating the built environment, land-use planning, resource flows and manufacturing, and social and economic institutions (found at www.conservationeconomy.net). This pattern language is now being used to catalyze and coordinate regional sustainability efforts. Stuart is a co-founder of the firm Sustainable Systems Design, where he currently works to help clients including banks, schools, planning agencies, and community groups integrate sustainability into their buildings, operations, and strategic thinking. He is the co-author (with Sim Van der Ryn) of *Ecological Design*, which provides a visionary overview of the ecological re-design of products, buildings, and landscapes. He holds a doctorate in the new science of complex systems from University of California at Berkeley, and has taught at Berkeley, Naropa Institute, and Antioch University in Seattle.

Ralph DiNola
Setting the Standard

As a senior design consultant for Portland General Electric's Green Building Services, Ralph DiNola serves as a project manager and green building consultant on numerous LEED registered projects. He has extensive experience with the LEED documentation process, and also assists in conceptual design for green building strategies, green product specifications, and project feasibility studies. Ralph specializes in facilitating green building workshops, eco-charrettes, and in delivering LEED Advanced Training Workshops as a LEED Advanced Faculty Member. He was the project manager for LEED documentation of the Natural Capital Center, and was instrumental in developing documentation for Viridian Place, the first LEED certified building in the Pacific Northwest.

Eugénie Frerichs
Editor; Introduction; Water; Community by Design

As the founding Madame de la Maison for the Natural Capital Center, Eugénie Frerichs worked closely with the community of tenants to bring to life the concepts and ideas of the conservation economy. She was closely involved with the development of educational and interpretive materials for the building, including an in-depth *Materials Guide* which highlights the stories of several of the green materials used throughout the building, and the *Field Guide to the Natural Capital Center*. Eugénie began her work with Ecotrust by researching, designing, and overseeing the installation of plants for the 6,000 square foot green roof, and she assisted with development and monitoring of the Natural Capital Center's stormwater management plan. Eugénie is a Northwest native, but has since fled to the hills of Telluride, Colorado. She holds a B.A. in Art History from The Colorado College.

Erin Kellogg
Editor; Introduction; Energy

From 1992 to 1997 Erin Kellogg served as Policy and Communications Director for Ecotrust, where she oversaw the writing, editing, design, and production of Ecotrust's publications including brochures, annual reports, scientific papers, and popular books and reports. She also coordinated media relations, working with journalists on stories in local and regional papers up and the down the West Coast; in *Time* magazine, *The Economist*, and *In Business*;

and on NPR's "All Things Considered." Erin then served as Vice President for Ecotrust Canada, running day-to-day operations and overseeing its community and regional programs. She most recently co-wrote the 2000 Founders of a New Northwest book for Sustainable Northwest. Erin holds a Masters degree from Yale's School of Forestry and Environmental Studies, and earned her B.A. from Yale College. She co-chaired the board of the Food Alliance from 1995 to 1997, and served on the board of the Prince William Sound Science Center in Alaska from 1995 to 2000.

Bob Naito

Working with History; The Renovation; Energy

Bob Naito formed Naito Development LLC in 2003 to develop commercial real estate in Portland and Seattle. Current projects include One Waterfront Place, a 256,000 square foot Class A office building that is designed to exceed the LEED Gold requirements. From 1997 though 2003, Bob was employed at Heritage Consulting Group, which provides historic rehabilitation consulting services at the national level. He served as the principal-in-charge for Heritage in its role as the fee developer of the Natural Capital Center. For the prior 20 years he worked in real estate for his family-owned business that specialized in the rehabilitation of historic buildings in Portland, Oregon. During that time he worked closely with his father, Bill Naito, a prominent civic leader and real estate entrepreneur, on projects that totaled over 2,000,000 square feet of office space and apartments. Bob is the founding president of the Portland Classical Chinese Garden and chaired the fundraising campaign for this $12.5 million project. He also served on the board of a number of local organizations including the Housing Authority of Portland, the Portland Metropolitan Chamber of Commerce, and the Portland Building Owners and Managers Association. Bob has a B.A. from Harvard College and an MBA from Stanford Business School.

Michael O'Brien

Energy

Michael O'Brien is a Green Building Specialist for the City of Portland's Green Building program, G/Rated, where he provides technical review and program development services. Before working for the city, he worked with the Northwest Energy Efficiency Alliance, where he helped to create 'betterbricks.com,' a website and outreach campaign that promotes the awareness of the health and productivity advantages of high-efficiency buildings. Michael also helped to create Portland General Electric's Earth Smart™ program, which has sparked numerous green buildings and homes throughout the city of Portland. He is regionally recognized as an authority on residential energy efficiency and indoor air quality.

Melissa Tatge

Book design, layout, and production

Melissa Tatge has accumulated a myriad of skills as a graphic designer through years of working for advertising and graphic design firms in New York City and Savannah, GA, as well as running her own company developing web sites and marketing solutions for small companies and non-profit organizations. Since 2001, Melissa has been putting her experience to work for Ecotrust as Creative Director, developing educational displays for the Natural Capital Center as well as innovative and effective communications for all of the organization's ambitious programs. Melissa received her B.A. in Politics from New York University in 1992. She has studied Graphic Design at Parson's School of Design and the School of Visual Arts; Product Design at the Savannah College of Art and Design; and Web Design at the Pacific Northwest College of Art. Never one to turn down an opportunity to explore new media, this is her first book design.

Bettina von Hagen

Editor; Introduction; The Renovation; Materials

Bettina von Hagen manages Ecotrust's Natural Capital Fund, a $20 million fund that invests in key businesses and initiatives in the conservation economy, and was the project manager for the Natural Capital Center redevelopment. Bettina also directs Ecotrust's forestry program which includes an initiative to increase the flow of wood products from sustainably managed forests to green building projects in the region. Bettina has edited and written a number of publications on sustainable forestry and the conservation economy, including co-editing *The Rain Forests of Home*, which describes the ecological, economic, and social conditions of the coastal temperate rain forest. She joined Ecotrust in 1993 to help launch Ecotrust's partnership with Shorebank Corporation. Prior to joining Ecotrust, Bettina was a Vice President at First Interstate Bank of Oregon. Bettina holds an MBA from the University of Chicago and a B.A. from the University of the Pacific. She currently serves on the boards of Forest Trends, Climate Trust, and Friends of Opal Creek.

The *Rebuilt Green* editing, design and production team. From left: Erin Kellogg, Bettina von Hagen, Melissa Tatge, and Eugénie Frerichs.

G/Rated

G/Rated is a program of Portland's Office of Sustainable Development's Green Building Division. Created in partnership with the Sustainable Development Commission and the input of over 160 local developers, architects, engineers, affordable housing providers, advocacy groups, and city employees in 1999, G/Rated has grown to be one of the most comprehensive and credible resources for green building practices and research in the United States.

The program was designed with two goals:

1. To expand market demand by educating building industry professionals and the public about the benefits of green building.
2. To make green building practices easier to implement by reducing regulatory and financial barriers while developing technical services and resources for building industry professionals.

G/Rated services and resources include:

- Personalized technical assistance
- Web-based resource and research center
- Best practices, specifications, and resource guides
- On-line green products and services directory
- Financial incentives
- Case studies and technical briefs

Visit www.green-rated.org to learn more.

Naito Development LLC

Naito Development LLC was launched by Bob Naito in 2003 to develop commercial real estate in Portland, Oregon and Seattle, Washington. Current projects include One Waterfront Place, a LEED Gold Class A office building located in Portland's River District (www.onewaterfrontplace.com), and developing a headquarters and training center in Seattle for an international non-profit organization.

Naito's development experience, focused largely on the rehabilitation of historic buildings in Portland, includes:

- The conversion of a vacant downtown department store into a specialty shopping center
- The historic rehabilitation of an 800,000 square foot Montgomery Ward catalog warehouse into an office building for large back-office tenants
- New construction of a 301-unit apartment complex on the Willamette River north of downtown Portland
- A joint venture with a non-profit organization to convert a historic riverfront grain mill into offices and laboratories
- A number of smaller historic rehabilitations in Portland

Contact Bob Naito at bob@naitodev.com.

Green Building Services

Green Building Services is a professional consulting practice dedicated to helping clients create better living, learning, and working environments.

GBS' professional team includes architects, engineers, and interior designers. With their first-hand knowledge of the design and construction process, GBS helps foster cross-discipline communication and problem-solving to reach integrated design solutions for high-performance buildings.

Green building technologies and practices are evolving rapidly to meet the demands of this dynamic industry and GBS team members are at the forefront of this effort. GBS brings technical expertise in high-performance building systems and materials and will help you select the right strategies to achieve your project goals.

GBS offers a range of services including:

- Design consultations for owners and architects to realize green objectives, including eco-charettes, high-performance building consulting, and LEED project management.
- Training in sustainable design, green construction, green products, and facility management practices.
- Facility audits and consultation to help building owners and facility managers create and maintain healthy, efficient, and productive spaces.
- Sustainable design reports and guidelines, including energy modeling and engineer reports.

Visit www.greenbuildingservices.com for more information.

Cascadia Region Green Building Council

The Cascadia Region Green Building Council (Cascadia) builds capacity for sustainable buildings and communities in Oregon, Washington and British Columbia. We serve the Cascadia bioregion, 750,000 square miles of watersheds demarcated by the migration of salmon and flow of water to the Pacific Ocean through the greatest temperate rain forests on the planet.

The US Green Building Council has altered the marketplace with LEED, the industry standard certification system for green building. Within the bioregion, we adapt and amplify this national initiative to give it regional relevance.

Cascadia promotes the design, construction and operation of buildings that are environmentally responsible, profitable and healthy places to live and work. Through education, research and information exchange, Cascadia is leading the region's transformation to green building practices. Begun in December 1999, Cascadia has made great strides in transforming the market through strategic public and private partnerships. One of three inaugural chapters of the USGBC, Cascadia is recognized as the umbrella organization for green building in the region.

Buildings are the infrastructure of community — influencing the way we work, live, learn, gather and recreate. Their development both reflects and dictates our view of ourselves in relation to the outer world. We believe in this initiative so strongly that we've not only co-sponsored this book, we've established our first office in the Natural Capital Center, thanks to the generous support of Metafore, the Office of Sustainable Development, and Ecotrust.

Bioregionalism views people as part of an overall ecosystem where success is based on establishing long term balance with natural systems. Cascadia strives to bring this ethic to our work, emphasizing green building's economic, environmental, and community benefits. Cascadia envisions a day when green building strategies do more than just diminish impacts, but instead actively promote solutions within the landscape, buildings, and people that make up our communities.

Contact Cascadia Region Green Building Council at info@cascadiagbc.org or (503) 228-5533.

Walsh Construction

Walsh Construction Co. has brought quality and craftsmanship to the Northwest construction industry for over 40 years. Specializing in commercial and educational facilities and affordable multi-family housing, we have also built a strong reputation for rehabilitation and historic preservation. Our broad portfolio reaches across all public, private and non-profit market sectors. With the completion of the Jean Vollum Natural Capital Center, Walsh has become a regional leader in sustainable construction and is one of only a handful of general contractors with a Certified LEED Professional permanently on staff.

We believe in collaborating with developers, architects, and government agencies that share the same vision of quality and value that has distinguished our work for 40+ years, and in building strong relationships with people — whether they are our clients, architects, partners, or employees. This philosophy is paramount to building projects successfully. An ever-growing list of repeat clients serves as an indicator of our high standards and our investment in long-lasting relationships.

Since 1961, WCC has grown steadily, adding museums, medical facilities and high-end resorts to our list of capabilities, and deepening skills in wood frame and steel construction, structural masonry, and poured-in-place concrete. Our success has allowed us to expand geographically as well — with offices in Seattle and Sacramento. We build throughout the western United States.

Walsh provides valuable, comprehensive pre-construction services, with a "menu" of services to more specifically identify the activities and timing of our efforts from a project's initial concept through construction drawings. In addition, our diverse experience can provide an unusual depth of cost and construction detail knowledge.

As one of the largest employers of skilled labor in the local construction market, we offer our own full-time excavation, concrete, framing, finish carpentry and painting crews. With in-house crews who self-perform the work, we can create shorter and more accurate schedules and uphold our high standards of quality work. We continually bid our self-performed work against the market to ensure our prices are competitive.

Walsh's solid reputation reflects a strong set of values which drive all of our efforts — fair business practices; openness and cooperation among all parties; a spirit of innovation; and consistent, high quality work.

Visit www.walshconstructionco.com for further information.

ACKNOWLEDGEMENTS

Many thanks for financial support to the Bank of America Foundation, Bank of the West, Dick Jaffe, the U.S. Green Building Council, and the Flora Family Foundation and to co-sponsors Walsh Construction, Green Building Services, City of Portland G/Rated program, Cascadia Green Building Council, and Naito Development LLC.

We are grateful to Sarah Davies for early help with funding, Charlotte Gallagher for support and encouragement, Andy Frichtl of Interface Engineering and to Paul Schwer at PAE Consulting Engineers, Inc. for guidance on the Energy chapter, and to University of Oregon Architecture students Anita Washko, Kathy Bash, Janelle Black, Ted Shiro, and Yasayuki Yanagisawa working under the guidance of Dr. Alison Kwok and to Elaine Aye and Ralph DiNola from Green Building Services for suggestions on the Materials chapter. We would also like to thank Jeff Wartelle, Ted Wolf, Rod Stevens, Christine Ervin, Brian Kirkpatrick, Georgia Kirkpatrick, and Sophia von Hagen for support and helpful suggestions. Thanks to Dan Lipow for being our man on the spot in New York and to Dan Imhoff for support and for his inspiring green building book Building with Vision. We are grateful as well to Michael Wilhelm, Lowell Downey, Jim Hench, Charley Dewberry, Thor Peterson, Lucia Athens, the City of Seattle and the Friends of the Napa River for help in locating and contributing images and information.

As always, we are deeply indebted to our colleagues at Ecotrust, especially Eileen Brady for brainstorming the book title, Kara Orvieto, Howard Silverman, Dagmar Carstensen, Ofelia Svart, Kim Burkland, Chris Sanford, and Gabe Carleton-Barnes for technical support with dramatic flair. Lizzie Grossman provided skillful proofreading and valuable suggestions.

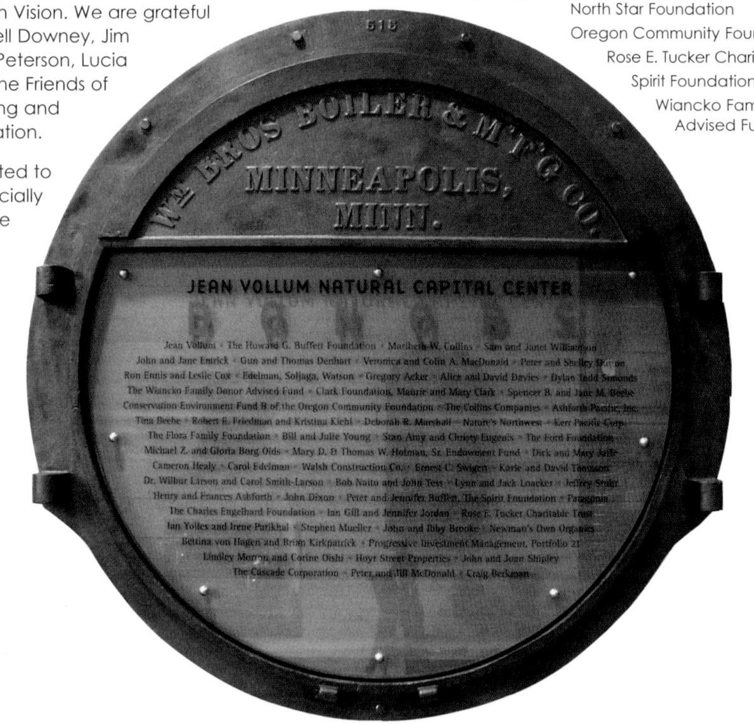

NATURAL CAPITAL CENTER DONORS

Of course, the book would not be possible without the building. We are deeply grateful to the funders and supporters of the Natural Capital Center, especially Jean Vollum and Jane Jacobs, who were there at the beginning. Without their inspiration and support, the Natural Capital Center would not have been redeveloped. Many thanks to:

Foundations:
- H.G.Buffett Foundation
- Clark Foundation
- Charles Engelhard Foundation
- Flora Family Foundation
- Ford Foundation
- Bill Healy Foundation
- Mary D. & Thomas W. Holman Sr. Endowment Fund
- North Star Foundation
- Oregon Community Foundation
- Rose E. Tucker Charitable Trust
- Spirit Foundation
- Wiancko Family Donor Advised Fund

Individuals:
- Greg Acker
- Anonymous
- Henry & Frances Ashforth
- Spencer B. & Jane M. Beebe
- Tina Beebe
- Craig Berkman
- Elizabeth Brooke
- Maribeth Collins
- Leslie Cox & Ron Ennis
- Alice & David Davies
- Gun & Tom Denhart
- John Dixon
- Peter & Shelly Dutton
- Carol Edelman
- John & Jane Emrick
- Robert Friedman & Kristina Kiehl
- Mary & Dick Jaffe
- Carolyn & Jack Loacker
- Veronica & Colin Macdonald
- Deborah Marshall
- Peter & Jill McDonald
- Lindley Morton & Corinne Oishi
- Steve Mueller
- W. Robert Naito
- Michael & Gloria Olds
- John & Joan Shipley
- Dylan Simonds
- Carol Smith-Larson & Wilbur Larson
- Jeff Stuhr
- Ernest Swigert
- Karie & David Thomson
- Jean Vollum
- Bettina von Hagen & Brian Kirkpatrick
- Sam & Janet Williamson
- Ian Yolles & Irene Parikhal
- Bill & Julie Young

Corporations:
- Anonymous Corp.
- Ashforth Pacific
- Cascade Corp.
- Collins Pine
- Edelman, Soljaga, Watson
- Green Gables Corp.
- Hoyt St. Properties
- The Joinery
- Kerr Pacific, Inc.
- Nature's Fresh Northwest
- Newman's Own Organics
- Nike, Inc.
- The Collins Companies
- Patagonia, Inc.
- Progressive Investment Management, Portfolio 21
- Walsh Construction Co.

Natural Capital Center benefactor Jean Vollum